IT **IS** ALL IN YOUR HEAD:
A Monograph on Wellness for the New Millennium

JORY F. GOODMAN, M. D.

SYNAPSE PUBLISHING, LLC

SYNAPSE PUBLISHING, LLC
P. O Box 1027
Amherst, New Hampshire 03031

ISBN # 0-9725152-0-8

To:

Carola, Gabriella, Marissa and Jory, who comprise my universe,

and

Joseph A. Harter, M. D.
The Compleat Physician

IT **IS** ALL IN YOUR HEAD:
A Monograph on Wellness for the New Millennium

TABLE OF CONTENTS

INTRODUCTION

This is the second edition of <u>IT **IS** ALL IN YOUR HEAD:</u> <u>A Monograph on Wellness for the New Millennium</u>. The first edition was copyrighted in 1998. It was not published but was circulated amongst many physicians and neuroscientists as well as lay people for their review, comments and criticism. The feedback received helped the author immeasurably in the reorganization and refinement of the present second edition. That rough draft was also sent to some agents and publishers for their review. Unfortunately this lead to some unexpectedly broad circulation of the unpublished first edition to the point that other individuals have begun to talk about the core concept of this book, The Neurosomatic Syndrome, in print and on the World Wide Web.

Nonetheless the author has improved and updated the content of the second edition for it's present publication. The information herein is of enormous importance to millions of people insofar as they have suffered greatly from inaccurate diagnoses and ineffective or frankly improper treatment.

Identification and understanding of The Neurosomatic Syndrome enables physicians and patients to have a much better and more coherent grasp of what has been wrong for so long and how best and most simply to fix it. Cognizance of the real differences between the conceptualization of a mind-body illness in contrast to a brain-body illness is a step forward of great magnitude.

A necessary part of this book is a discussion of mal-treatment, particularly with a group of drugs called the Serotonin Selective Re-uptake Inhibitors (SSRIs). These widely prescribed and widely over prescribed drugs have inflicted enormous distress upon society, affected negatively the lives of millions of people in more ways than they understand, and literally stunted the emotional, psychological and social growth of millions of children and adolescents.

As much as you learn from this book, and as strongly you may identify with the case examples herein, remember that it is a book. If you are a person afflicted with The Neurosomatic Syndrome, do not self treat. If you are an individual at present under treatment which you may think is less than optimal or in fact improper, do not alter this treatment yourself. Always seek the help of an expert psychiatrist, or neuropsychiatrist.

Hopefully your understanding of The Neurosomatic Syndrome and it's proper treatment will improve and enrich your life, diminish your suffering and side effects, and decrease your overall need for health care, consultation, and pharmaceuticals.

Jory F. Goodman, M. D.

IT **IS** ALL IN YOUR HEAD:
A Monograph on Wellness for the New Millennium

CHAPTER ONE
HEAD GAMES

What seems to be the problem? You need more serotonin, don't you? Isn't that the answer, the cure? To be sure you were misled when you thought you had hypoglycemia, then chronic fatigue syndrome, and some fibromyalgia on top of your migraine, headaches, irritable bowel syndrome, peptic ulcers, insomnia, moodiness, anxiety, poor concentration, not enough pep. Yep, that's the key, serotonin, right? Or was that melatonin? Or dihydroepiendosterone, chondroitin, or tryptophan? Well what about St. John's Wort; you can't forget about St. John's Wort, can you? By the time you finish this book, hopefully you will.

We live in the information age. It's all over the place; information. Facts and fallacies, opinions and beliefs, answers and beyond. In print, broadcast and on television and radio, and on the Internet, you are informed whether you want to be or not.

Many believe that we have too much of it – information – and not enough understanding. Without sententious sound bites from disconnected talking heads how does one add all of it up into a comprehensible, useful whole. Can one ever hope to put it all together, or enough of it, to reach a useful truth.

This dizzying bombardment affects most areas of our lives: politics, education, the economy, and your health to name a few. I am a doctor, old-fashioned to be sure, and I'm interested in your health. What we are going to do here is look at how a huge amount of simple, obvious, right in front of your nose information is missed, misunderstood, misapplied, and often just plain ignored – to your great pain and suffering. Most of this information about you, your health and your treatment is not new. Your doctors studied most of it in medical school; basic physiology, anatomy, endocrinology and pharmacology. It's been written about for at least most of the last century. And you bring it to their offices daily. Failure to grasp this information, and frequently the failure to put it all together, leads to fragmented, contradictory, and ineffective if not damaging treatment. The purpose here is understanding and solutions. As we proceed we will look into the past and learn much. There will be no attempt to denounce present theory only to "discover" it anew with a jazzy new moniker and a goofy explanation. Mostly we will discover what we knew or should have known all already, as we establish connections between the things that are already connected.

Amongst the information overload there are facts, fables, fantasies, falsehoods and advertisements. The goal here is threefold. First: to identify a heretofore misunderstood and poorly managed constellation of problems as a single illness with a coherent and unitary treatment approach. Second: to expand upon the typical treatment of those problems and the new treatment of the illness. Third: to comment, at times acerbically on the deleterious effects of present treatment with a critical view towards some of the social, political and economic forces that have driven misunderstanding and mismanagement.

As you read on you will very likely see yourself or at least a number of people you know. And as you continue and understand the concepts then you or at least some of those folks can be helped to a happier, healthier life with a great deal less treatment and cost than you or those folks now bear.

There are no panaceas here. Nor any grand preposterous claims that one secret elixir will fix the world. This is about a group of ills and afflictions that trouble a great number of people throughout their lives. Rarely fatal, but uniformly unpleasant and disruptive to health and happiness, these "presenting complaints" are the bread and butter of doctor visits. They absorb a fortune in health care costs, another fortune in decreased productivity, and an incalculable cost in human pain and suffering. Often dubbed as functional, psychosomatic or psychophysiologic, and not often successfully treated ("why don't you just buck up and learn to live with it?!"), we schlep back to the pharmacy for yet another three or four more pricey miracle drugs and another grab bag of side effect surprises.

Below there is a list of complaints. If you see anything that's troubled you, please read on. There will also be a list of descriptive terms, often applied in a derisive or derogatory manner, to individuals who make these complaints. If you've been labeled with any of these, read on.

1) MOOD DISORDERS, INCLUDING DEPRESSION, DYSTHYMIA, CYCLOTHYMIA, AND BIPOLAR
2) HEADACHES; INCLUDING MIGRAINE, STRESS, AND MIXED HEADACHES
3) IRRITABLE BOWEL SYNDROME/COLITIS
4) PEPTIC ULCERS/GASTROESOPHAGEAL REFLUX DISEASE
5) SLEEP PROBLEMS
6) ANXIETY DISORDER INCLUDING PANIC ATTACKS AND SOCIAL ANXIETY
7) EATING DISORDERS, PARTICULARLY BULIMIA AND CARBOHYDRATE CRAVINGS
8) HIGH BLOOD PRESSURE
9) ATTENTION DEFICIT HYPERACTIVITY DISORDER, ALL SUBTYPES
10) FIBROMYALGIA/MYOFASCIAL PAIN SYNDROME

Have you ever been told that you are too high-strung, too tightly wound, a Type A personality, too intense, not easy going enough, can't relax, don't know how to just go along, go with the flow? Has anyone ever said that you are a hypochondriac, that you somatacize too much? These and many other put-downs have been used for generations. They apply particularly to those who find themselves on the above list.

It's rather presumptuous don't you think to address so many seemingly unrelated problems in one little book. Maybe, if you haven't given it much thought. But then, that's precisely why, if you do think about it, the relations and relevance become coherent. In the next chapters we will accomplish our goal of a better understanding of these problems. Along the way there will be references to the pertinent fundamental and basic sciences involved as well as some discussions of anatomy, physiology, chemistry, and pharmacology. But have no fear, these will be handled in a way that will cause you no distress. Common sense definitions and descriptions will be offered, and a few interesting historical perspectives unearthed. We will look at a symptom check list and begin to see how these seemingly unrelated entities cluster together.

Composite case histories are provided that are consistent with each and every one of the target symptoms noted on the above list. These case histories may help you identify more clearly and concretely what you have experienced. We will see how these various complaints tend to come together. The approach is from many different perspectives. We will begin to see and understand the underlying source of these problems as a unitary and discrete problem that can be addressed in a simple and coherent fashion.

Each complaint will be discussed independently and examples of the past and present treatments given. However with our new understanding of these problems we will be able to put forth a simple and unified approach that deals with the source of these problems rather than each and every problem individually.

These problems will be seen as <u>symptoms</u> of one central illness rather as independent illnesses themselves.

An objective look will be taken at the maltreatment so rampant, and how a thoughtful, balanced and actually holistic approach is more effective, safer and easier than the organ/symptom focus of most practices now extant.

CHAPTER TWO
HOW TO READ THIS BOOK

In earlier drafts of this book it became apparent that it is necessary to provide clear and straightforward language and descriptions for the lay reader. At the same time it is necessary to provide scientific medical data to support the thesis put forward. It is not my goal to obfuscate or confuse these issues. Nor do I wish to seem pedantic or condescending to the reader. Therefore the book is written as a relatively short book with long footnotes.

There are two typefaces. The regular typeface which you are reading at this time will contain the basic story. Case histories, discussions, and solutions will be put forth. There will be some medical and scientific terms used. They will be defined as simply and succinctly as possible. No detailed scientific discussions will be present.

In the italics which look like this, the body of the scientific and medical discussion will occur. Thus, those who have the need or interest to read the supporting data may do so.

What this means for you is that if you are willing to take my word for it that the science and medicine put forth here are fundamentally sound and accurate you can bypass all of the italics and have a very quick read from complaint to cure. Yet at any point along the way you can delve as deeply as you wish into the medical science, and review the data to your own satisfaction.

Let us now proceed.

CHAPTER THREE
REVIEW OF SYMPTOMS

     Traditionally a physician does a review of the symptoms at the beginning of a thorough examination. This medical version of twenty questions enables one to rule in or rule out a panoply of diagnostic possibilities and home in on what seems to be the basic problem. Below is a list of complaints or problems similar to that noted in the first chapter. I suggest that you go through it methodically, checking off each and every item noted that has troubled you, past or present, mild or severe. Each of these items will be elaborated upon in great detail in the chapters that follow. As we proceed you may want to revise your scores. That's fine. Go right ahead. Then go through the list a second time and try to quantify the severity of each complaint as objectively as you can. For simplicity we will use a scale of zero to three. Zero means not significant. One means, on average, mild. Two means, on average, moderate. Three means, on average, severe. Since all of the items on the list tend to wax and wane over time, or to go in cycles, try to mark the worst or highest average. Don't put a three if you only had one really bad headache in your life, unless it lasted a very long time and was not related to an in-law.

1) HEADACHES   0 1 2 3

2) MOOD PROBLEMS   0 1 2 3

3) IRRITABLE BOWEL SYNDROME/COLITIS   0 1 2 3

4) PEPTIC ULCERS/REFLUX ESOPHAGITIS   0 1 2 3

5) SLEEP PROBLEMS	0 1 2 3
6) ANXIETY PROBLEMS	0 1 2 3
7) EATING PROBLEMS	0 1 2 3
8) HIGH BLOOD PRESSURE	0 1 2 3
9) A.D.H.D	0 1 2 3
10) FIBROMYALGIA/MYOFASCIAL PAIN	0 1 2 3

"So what?" say you. Everybody's had a headache, aches and pains, an upset stomach, a bad night's sleep, hard times. One can't get through finals, income tax time, or a season with the Chicago Cubs without one or another.

Absolutely correct, say I. As would most of the people on the planet. Except that is not to what I refer, to which several million folks will agree. The frequency, chronicity, and intensity of distress are far more than that engendered by another losing season at Wrigley Field. A stoic, stalwart mesomorph with a cast iron stomach and nerves of steel will score a two or three. Up to six is a gray zone, possibly to be refined as we proceed. If you accumulate more than six points you're sure to find yourself in one of the case examples to follow, and some help in the following chapters.

CHAPTER FOUR
BASIC SCIENCE

HOMEOSTASIS.

 Walter Cannon, MD a famed physiologist in the first half of the twentieth century coined the phrase and waxed eloquently about it in his classic THE WISDOM OF THE BODY. It was written in 1932. Homeostasis describes the constant effort of the bodies many systems to stay in balance. Not static or inflexible, but maintaining a dynamic equilibrium in a variable but generally narrow range, these homeostatic mechanisms are necessary for survival. Obvious examples would include such functions as your body temperature, blood pressure and pulse. Less obvious to many might be the systems which maintain the balance of electrolytes (sodium, potassium, calcium, etc...) in your blood, or the correct balance of oxygen and carbon dioxide. Outside of the normal range bad things happen.

 The systems are myriad and interrelated. Throughout the body are a fascinating array of sensors and servomechanisms which monitor and communicate. Messages are sent in many ways. These include nerve impulses, hormones, other chemical messengers, and the constant monitoring of levels and status of everything in and around you. Balance is achieved by the maintenance of a dynamic tension between complementary, or in some cases contrary systems. Thus a bio-physiological yin and yang exists in concert with the spiritual one. This is homeostasis.

 What seems to have been lost, or forgotten, is that the ultimate sensor, receptor, servant and all around boss is your brain. You may not have thought about it, and you usually don't have to, for your brain to monitor, analyze, supervise, adjust, stabilize, compensate, re-equilibrate, arbitrate and ride herd on a gazillion bits of information every microsecond or so and decide just what to do. Be advised, your brain aims to establish and maintain what it has been genetically programmed to know as "NORMAL". If you are born with a bit of a glitch somewhere in your genetic code, your normal baseline might be off a bit, and/or your brain's capacity to maintain your homeostasis might be a bit wacky. And if we factor in the common human foolishness of ignoring your body – what it tells you and what it needs – and use your glorious "higher cortical functions" to override what your brain gallantly tries to accomplish, your codes don't matter and you suffer.

THE HYPOTHALAMIC – PITUITARY- ADRENAL AXIS (HPA)
  The hypothalamus is a small piece of your brain, right beneath the thalamus. It, the hypothalamus is comprised of an immense cluster of nuclei (pleural for nucleus). These nuclei are the prime servomechanisms, thermostats if you will for your entire being. Information is received in multiple ways: from neuronal projections (nerve bundles that gather and transmit data from other parts of the brain); from monitoring levels in the blood of innumerable substances; and from feedback loops from other components of the HPA.
  The pituitary gland snuggles up under the hypothalamus. It receives chemical messages, called releasing factors, from the hypothalamus, which tell the pituitary to produce and release its hormones, which then circulate throughout the body and tell their target organs what to do. Amongst those target organs are the thyroid, ovaries, testicles and adrenal glands. The target organ does its thing, the hypothalamus monitors it, and homeostasis is maintained.

IT **IS** ALL IN YOUR HEAD:
A Monograph on Wellness for the New Millennium

THE AUTONOMIC NERVOUS SYSTEM

The autonomic nervous system is studied in high school biology, not to mention undergraduate biology and physiology courses. It is also called the involuntary nervous system because it controls a bunch of things we can't control with our sophisticated uniquely human higher cortical function. It's not cool or sexy. In fact it's rather simple and mechanical. But since we can't control it anyhow, why bother with it at all?

What does it do? It modulates, controls, balances and maintains homeostasis amongst innumerable critical physiologic systems and processes absolutely necessary for life; nothing more. If it's a bit erratic, or imbalanced, you are miserable. When it really goes awry you suffer terribly and often die, as do those unfortunate enough to have been born with a genetically transmitted disorder Familial Dysautonomia (big glitch in the code!). And, of all the nerve, you have no voluntary control over it. None. Zip. Zero. But it can cause you grief. It can and does give you all sorts of signals and information about what it wants and needs, and what would be good for you, or else, but being really smart and superior organisms who generally know better about everything and in particular about what we want to do and need, we ignore something as primitive as the autonomic nervous system which after all governs the function of lesser species and do what we want when we want and then want to know why we seem to be having a problem. The ANS has two component parts which function simultaneously in complementary and antagonistic ways. The sympathetic nervous system has always been called the fight/flight system. It alerts and arouses, gets ready to fight or run for your life. It squeezes adrenaline (also called epinephrine) out of your adrenal glands. And . . . heart rate goes up; blood vessels constrict; voluntary muscles tense; blood pressure increases; sensory vigilance heightens; and energy is consumed as metabolism increases. Ex Vacuo of this experience is called ***ANXIETY***

By the way, as the sympathetic nervous system activates, it shuts down its cohort the parasympathetic nervous system. The PNS quietly maintains many necessary vital functions; digestion and bowel function are a couple. As PNS activity increases, yep, heart rate goes down; blood vessels dilate; blood pressure drops; vigilance diminishes; and energy consumption decreases with metabolism.

Keep in mind, these two systems are antagonistic. When one's a go the other's a no. You can't do both at once, even if you want to. Oh, and by the way, bouncing back and forth unnaturally between them, preventing a normal homeostasis to exist, gets your attention swiftly.

CHAPTER FIVE
NEUROSOMATIC

The Neurosomatic Syndrome encompasses a collection of ailments and afflictions, ostensibly unrelated, often which are chronic troublesome problems, which cause an incredible amount of pain and suffering, a huge amount of money both in terms of health care dollars spent as well as lost income and decreased productivity. All have been treated in a symptom organ focused fashion with a veritable slew of drugs. A few have achieved the status of an illness per se, mood disorders or ADHD, and some are considered syndromes or symptoms such as fibromyalgia or insomnia, but virtually all continue to be considered functional, psychosomatic or a sign of a weak character.

We will review some case histories and complaints. Along the way we will learn a few tidbits of history and some anecdotes and will learn some more as we proceed. There will be a necessary debunking of the SSRI's. We will need to diminish their importance and see them simply as amongst viable treatment options for certain problems after careful diagnosis and treatment planning has occurred. At this point I will make a firm assertion that there is a very clear and obvious illness heretofore not identified that has at its core a central nervous system chemical imbalance, primarily in the noradrenalin transmitter pathway, that has a multiplicity of <u>symptomatic</u> presentations which may vary from patient to patient and that may vary within a patient over with time. It has both primary symptoms and secondary symptoms. Many of its parts have, over time, been deemed functional or psychosomatic or psychophysiologic. I have selected the term **Neurosomatic** to reflect a true **biological basis** in the brain which manifests as a smorgasbord of physical symptoms. There is nothing psychosomatic functional or psychophysiologic about this. These somatic manifestations are very clearly a function of a biological neurochemical problem.

Below we will review in careful detail the symptomatology that comprises this disorder. We will review case histories within the framework of this new formulation and be able to see the internal consistency inherent in this conceptualization as we refine a coherent treatment strategy that is much simpler than the polypharmacy regimens en vogue today. The treatment strategy is not symptom focused. Rather it is directed at the central mechanisms that are, in the parlance, out of whack. We will unearth some useful anecdotes and historical facts as we proceed. Why not have some fun and pop some balloons in the service of knowledge and truth?

First of all let's review some of the general concepts to which we have alluded earlier that will be pertinent as we proceed. These include the autonomic nervous system with its two components the sympathetic and parasympathetic elements. The hypothalamic pituitary adrenal axis is due for some examination as we proceed. And the abiding concept that is at the core of this is homeostasis. The body, the entire body (for those who need to be reminded the brain is a part of the body) struggles constantly to maintain homeostasis in everyone of its gazillion systems. It may be a tad off the mark at one place or another for innumerable reasons and as a result we experience one affliction or another.

To proceed we will do a review of systems/symptoms. We will combine the upper and lower gastrointestinal complaints into one group. Then we will form a grid which lists these problems on two axes. We will cross-reference each disorder to indicate how commonly symptoms of one problem are concurrent with those of another. The scale will be zero equals never; one equals occasionally; two equals often; and three equals usually. Later on we will examine this in depth. And we will begin to separate out some of the secondary symptoms from the primary cluster. As you look at the chart below keep in mind that the vertical list is the presenting problem and that the horizontal list are the associated complaints that are present if one bothers to ask. Recall both the current colloquial conceptualization of these diagnoses as well as those described in this book.

	MOOD	ANXI	ADHD	GI	HA	Sleep	EAT	HTN	Fibro
MOOD		3	3	2	3	3	3	2	2
ANXI	2		2	2	2	3	3	2	1
ADHD	3	3		2	2	3	2	2	1
GI	2	2	1		2	2	2	2	1
HA	2	2	2	2		2	1	2	1
Sleep	2	2	2	2	2		1	2	2
EAT	3	3	3	3	2	2		1	1
HTN	2	2	1	2	2	2	1		1
Fibro	3	2	2	2	3	3	1	2	

If we look at these data we see an interesting phenomenon. For the most part every problem seems to overlap with the others. Do I expect you to believe that no one ever has a headache, an ulcer, high blood pressure, insomnia, nerves, what have you, all by itself? Absolutely not. Certainly these entities can and do occur independently. The problem is that in most cases these problems are always seen as solitary, independent and unrelated. They are then treated as such; solitary independent and unrelated. When a problem exists in isolation it can and should be treated effectively. How many of you have gone to see a physician with one of these complaints? How often has the physician enquired about the possible presence of any of the other items on the list? If he has or if you have offered them up independently how often has the physician suggested that there might be a relationship between these complaints and that they might all respond to a single coherent treatment strategy (other than the onerous suggestion or implication that all of your complaints were neurotic, functional or psychosomatic and that you should see a therapist who hasn't a better clue than the physician as to what is happening).

Thus far I have described the patients and their complaints from a traditional symptom/organ focus. This means symptoms have been described in a discrete fashion, often referable to a specific organ system. Obviously headaches and the head would seem inseparable. Gastroesophageal reflux disease and the stomach and esophagus, irritable bowel syndrome and the intestines, are obvious. Many other symptoms such as depression, anxiety and attention deficit hyperactivity disorder are referable to the mind, brain, or character, depending upon the perspective of the observer. And all of this helps us understand the problem in diagnosis and treatment that we will unravel in the coming chapters.

Traditional mainstream medicine has become a symptom/organ focused practice. The patients complain of symptoms. Doctors enquire about the symptoms and on the basis of limited information make diagnoses usually attributable to one or another organ system and treat that symptom and/or that organ system.

There is a concept called multi-system disease. However in

present day medicine multi-system disease often means that there are multiple diseases which affect multiple systems (organ systems). There are some diseases which are acknowledged to affect multiple systems. Such things as multiple sclerosis, systemic lupus erythematosis, and Lyme disease are examples. Yet most of the time the concept of multi-system disease implies multiple diseases in multiple systems.

Today's physicians are trained in a system/organ focused model. Patient's complaints are narrowed down to a specific focus, that focus is identified as one or another organ system. Then that organ system is examined and treated. In today's managed care environment the evaluation is often cursory or nonexistent and the treatment is entirely symptom focused.

Specialty and subspecialty medicine exacerbates the problem. This is not to impugn the integrity or capability of specialists and sub-specialists. It will however identify a flaw in the system.

Some medical schools have second year medical students identify a major. They will focus their studies in a specific area such as pediatrics, internal medicine, surgery, family practice, or obstetrics and gynecology or psychiatry. These students will spend a great deal of elective time in those subjects.

Upon medical school graduation medical students become interns (or first year residents in the politically correct common parlance) and then residents, and then fellows. The old fashioned rotating internship has all but disappeared. A rotating internship exposed the intern to many areas of medicine including pediatrics, medicine, obstetrics and gynecology, psychiatry, orthopedics, infectious diseases, emergency medicine and so forth and so on. Today's internships are more focused into medicine or surgery or pediatrics. After one year of internship residents then specialize in one of these or other areas. Indeed some do specialize in family practice but that is problematic as well. Fellowships which occur after residency take specialization to yet another level such as gastroenterology, cardiology, neonatology, cardiothoracic surgery, and many others. The family practitioner does a residency having exposure to many of the core aspects in medicine and brief exposure to a variety of specialties.

Thus when a patient presents to a family practitioner, pediatrician, internist, or nurse practitioner, the practitioner homes in on the chief complaint. While a proper history, review of systems and examination will be performed the focus remains the chief complaint. This will be pursued vigorously with referral when appropriate to a specialist who will then focus more intensively on the specific complaint referable generally to a specific organ system. In part because of the narrow focus and in part because of territorial concerns the specialists often will not venture far beyond their narrow focus.

There is a joke in medicine today that family practitioners know less and less about more and more until they know nothing about everything while specialists know more and more about less and less until they know everything about nothing. This becomes almost true to the detriment of the patient.

A fresh and different perspective on your problems and the problems of the patients described in this book yields a very different understanding and a very different treatment course.

CHAPTER SIX
IT **IS** ALL IN YOUR HEAD

The title of this book, IT IS ALL IN YOUR HEAD, is a play on the old put down used to demean individuals with Neurosomatic claims. Obviously they were faking or making it up or couldn't deal with things, or were just hypochondriacs. So it was all in their head.

Actually it is all in your head. But it's not in your mind. It's in your brain.

Philosophers and theologists and other learned folks have debated and discussed and expostulated for centuries on the difference between the mind and the brain. I don't want to wax too philosophical so I'll try to keep it simple. The brain refers to a biophysiologic organ inside your head comprised of billions and billions of nerve cells called neurons. It is an electrochemical organ which sends electrical and chemical messages from one nerve cell to another and sends electrical and chemical messages to the entire body. At the same time it monitors and maintains homeostasis for the entire body.

The mind is an abstraction. An important abstraction but an abstraction nonetheless. The mind is your thoughts, feelings, desires, wishes, fears, beliefs, hopes, faith, and philosophy. The mind may also be a part of your spirit or your soul. I do not mean to belittle any of these concepts. However I find them of little utility or relevance in the discussion of Neurosomatics.

Until now the references and allusions to psychophysiologic, psychosomatic, hypochondriacal, and functional illness has been to say that it is a mind/body problem. Some flaw in the mind causes a patient to have, experience, exaggerate, or fabricate an illness with

physical/somatic complaints. All of that is incorrect.

The Neurosomatic Syndrome has its roots <u>in the brain</u>, not the mind. In fact I am convinced that to a significant degree there is a problem in the hypothalamic modulation of many of the body's systems.

As described previously the hypothalamus is a small piece of the brain that snuggles down under the brain in an area that is basically between your eyes and behind your nose. The pituitary gland snuggles up onto and beneath the hypothalamus.

Remember that the hypothalamus, in particular the anterior hypothalamus, contains a vast array of nuclei which function as the brain's sensors or thermostats. A vast preponderance of the body's activity is monitored and adjusted through the hypothalamus. This includes the functions of appetite, sleep, the body's endocrine function including all of the hypothalamic, pituitary adrenal axis and sex hormones as well, ultimate control and supervision over the autonomic nervous system which by extension affects blood pressure, pulse, heart rhythm, digestive functions, muscle tension and tone, body temperature, and the like.

The following is a list of observations that I have assembled over a period of years. All are known and proven scientifically. They have not been connected heretofore in a coherent manner. All of these bits and pieces of information have come together to support the concept of Neurosomatics and the importance of the anterior hypothalamus as a major center for this problem.

1. For most of the twentieth century it has been known that there is a dysfunction or imbalance or problem with the hypothalamic pituitary adrenal axis in patients with mood disorders.

2. For decades it has been known that in patients with various mood disorders there are abnormalities in measurements of hypothalamic function. These abnormalities have been discerned in the dexamethasone suppression test and the TRH infusion test. These have been difficult to understand and interpret and cause and effect relations have been unclear.

3.   Radioactively tagged methylphenidate, amphetamine, and cocaine will light up certain areas in the brain, in particular areas in the temporal lobes, frontal lobes, and anterior hypothalamus. The temporal and frontal areas are consistent with symptoms of mood disorder, anxiety disorder and attentional disorder. They hypothalamus itself is involved with problems of sleep and appetite. Meanwhile the drug used to treat narcolepsy, modafanil, lights up the anterior hypothalamus alone. Its effectiveness in ADHD and other Neurosomatic symptoms is less certain.

4.   Positron emission tomography (PET) scans done with radioactive methylphenidate given to patients with documented ADHD will show increased blood flow in the putamen, a part of the basal ganglia. We already know that there is increased uptake in the anterior hypothalamus. The increased blood flow in the putamen is a reaction to instructions from the hypothalamus.

5.   Obviously, if by inference, electroconvulsive therapy (ECT) stabilizes or corrects or readjusts imbalances in hypothalamic thermostats. Thus it is effective in the following:

a.   severe depression wherein we already know there is a problem with the hypothalamus

b.   syndrome of inappropriate antidiuretic hormone (SIADH) a disorder that may occur after a severe head injury amongst other causes. One of the hypothalamic hormones is over produced causing severe problems with fluid and electrolyte balance and renal function/urination. Quite often difficult to correct pharmacotherapeutically, ECT corrects this.

c.   ECT is highly effective in facilitating improvement and often long term stabilization in Parkinson's Disease/Paralysis Agitans. In true Parkinson's Disease there is a loss of dopaminergic neurons in the basal ganglia and an imbalance between dopaminergic and cholinergic transmission. When pharmacotherapeutic intervention fails, ECT is often quite effective at stabilizing the neuronal systems. Again by inference this may be attributable to hypothalamic adjustment.

d. ECT is effective and often life saving in neuroleptic malignant syndrome (NMS). This is an often fatal neurochemical imbalance which presents with hyperpyrexia (severe high fevers), delirium, elevated white blood cell count, significant elevations of creatine phospho-kinase (CPK, an enzyme released by muscle breakdown with intense muscle activity), cardiac arrhythmia's and renal failure. It is mediated centrally by fiddling with the dopamine system, generally by excessive dopamine blockade caused by antipsychotic medications, and some other psychotropic drugs.

e. ECT is effective in lethal catatonia. Lethal catatonia is a rare syndrome that presents somewhat similarly to neuroleptic malignant syndrome. It is unknown to most physicians hence usually not diagnosed and treated. It is 100% fatal unless treated with electroconvulsive therapy. Symptomatically it presents with fluctuations in mental state from normal clarity to lethargy to delirium and back and forth. Physiologically it presents with severe fluctuations in blood pressure, multiple cardiac arrhythmia's, and sudden death from stroke or cardiac arrhythmia or myocardial infarction. The prominent symptoms of lethal catatonia, as well as those of neuroleptic malignant syndrome are manifested by aberrations in the autonomic nervous system.

f. Although there is no good information extant I conjecture that ECT would be highly effective in the serotonin syndrome, a disorder caused by excessive build up of serotonin in the brain from serotonergic medications. It is symptomatically again somewhat similar in its presentation to neuroleptic malignant syndrome and lethal catatonia and can be fatal. I am aware of no good studies at this time which have applied ECT to this disorder.

The hypothalamus is an ancient part of the brain. By this I mean that the brain of chordate creatures has evolved over time from the simple rhombenephalon through the mesencephalon and finally to the diencephalon. What this means is that very primitive organisms have an hypothalamus and an autonomic nervous system. They may not think very much, and very likely they may not feel very much, but nonetheless they have this neurologic and physiologic anatomy. Higher cortical function is a product of the diencephalic brain, the cortex of man. Certainly other primates and some other mammals have evolved cortices and think and feel.

I do propose to state that the source of the Neurosomatic Syndrome is in the hypothalamus. I do believe that the hypothalamus plays a key role insofar as it is a clearing house. Virtually all of the brain's pathways and tracts and bundles eventually go through and/or communicate with the hypothalamus. Simultaneously all the rest of the body and its myriad systems are monitored by and overseen by the hypothalamus.

Thus when there is a problem in affect, mood, or anger that may have its seat in parts of the temporal lobes, in particular the hippocampus or amygdala, the imbalance manifest there has some impact on the hypothalamus and its maintenance of homeostasis in many of the body's vegetative functions including the autonomic nervous system and its effects on gastrointestinal function, vasomotor stability, and sleep.

In the same way problems in frontal lobe systems which affect attention, impulse control, and executive function clearly project back through the hypothalamus. And as it has already been stated there are nuclei in the hypothalamus which modulate and control such things as appetite and sleep.

In reality the Neurosomatic Syndrome is all in your head. It is not a mind/body problem. It is a brain/body problem.

CHAPTER SEVEN
MY TYPICAL EXAMINATION

HOW CAN I HELP YOU?

When patients come to my office they have innumerable presenting complaints. Often the presenting complaint is a symptom of an underlying problem. Certainly a complaint such as "I am depressed" may be both a primary symptom and a diagnosis. Similarly anxiety or panic attacks may be in and of themselves definitive statements. In every case it is necessary to perform a proper examination including a history and mental status examination to determine the diagnosis and correct treatment. It is not proper to treat the presenting complaint as a diagnosis.

In terms of the Neurosomatic Syndrome that we have identified in this book it is important to note that many patients have had many or all of the symptoms previously discussed. Certainly no one has ever made a connection between all of them for the patient before. In many cases many of the symptoms have been misdiagnosed and treated in a way that has been deleterious to the patient's well being. In other cases patients have had many of the problems although they have not known that they were problems.

For example many people do not know that they have a sleep problem until it has been corrected. If one has had non-restorative restless sleep, Periodic Limb Movement Disorder (PLMD) since birth they may deny vehemently any problem. Parents may describe their baby as a frisky active baby who was hard to put to sleep and who slept very little. A child may be described as light a sleeper who would flop around and tear the bed up every night. They are found upside down on the bed with the covers on the floor virtually every morning. But they don't think they have a sleep problem. Younger adults may continue this denial until they reach the age of forty or forty-five when they finally become so exhausted that they seek some sort of remedy.

The same case can be made for the aches and pains of putative fibromyalgia, the heartburn of gastroesophageal reflux disease, the sugar/carbohydrate cravings of thousands who are not frankly "bulimic", the irregular crampy bowels of irritable bowel syndrome that has never been diagnosed or treated because the patient has never complained, the undiagnosed and untreated anxiety and depressive complaints and of course the classic undiagnosed attention deficit disorder.

There will be an extensive discussion of the Serotonin Selective Reuptake Inhibitors (SSRI's) later in this book. Suffice to say that their application for many of the items on our list, from fibromyalgia to migraine headaches to anxiety and mood problems often promote worsening of symptoms, terrible side effects that require more drugs for treatment, and induce problems. The most classic example is the patient who presents with some symptoms of depression, anxiety and moodiness who actually has a Neurosomatic Syndrome with obvious ADHD, non-restorative sleep, headaches, bowel complaints and the like who is diagnosed as depressed and started on an SSRI. Within weeks the patient's moodiness increases and they become agitated, restless, with racing thoughts and an inability to sleep. Significant aggressiveness may be demonstrated as well. This condition is then identified as bipolar illness which generates prescriptions for potent mood stabilizers such as Depakote or Lithium, often with supplemental anti-psychotic drugs which cause more dopamine blockade, and the prescriptions escalate until the patient is completely neutralized and neutered.

Anxious ADHD patients are often misdiagnosed as having Obsessive Compulsive Disorder. Of course they are given SSRI's for the putative OCD and the same degenerative process occurs.

IT **IS** ALL IN YOUR HEAD:
A Monograph on Wellness for the New Millennium

Thus when a patient presents to my office there are certain things that I need to know in order to make a diagnosis. Below I will proceed with a typical examination with descriptive embellishment.

GOOD MORNING, HOW CAN I HELP YOU?

The patient's response is called the chief complaint. The symptom or problem that brings them to my office.

CHIEF COMPLAINT

This may be anxiety, depression, mood swings, interpersonal problems, sleep problems, the whole gamut of human experience. You can fill in your own chief complaint and then we'll proceed.

HISTORY OF PRESENT ILLNESS

How long has this been going on, what are the symptoms, was there a specific precipitant, has it happened before, how has it affected the patient's life and function and relationships, has it been treated previously, how and how effectively? Going through the chief complaint and history of present illness will often identify a multiplicity of symptoms consistent with the Neurosomatic Syndrome yet not previously noted by other clinicians or even the patient themselves.

SLEEP

I want to know a great deal about the patient's sleep. This information can be learned in just a few moments. Typically is there difficulty falling asleep? Is there early morning awakening? Critically is the sleep restorative? Does the patient typically wake up well refreshed or tired? Is the patient a restless sleep? Do they kick around a lot at night? Tear the covers up? Flail about? Kick their partner? That is classic Periodic Limb Movement

Disorder/Restless Legs Syndrome. A patient may not have any overt periodic limb movements but may demonstrate only bruxism, tooth grinding. It is remarkable how many patients have poor quality sleep and grind their teeth and go to dentists who give them bite blocks and examine their temporal mandibular joints and do not know that bruxism is a cardinal feature of a sleep disorder. Are there jerks and twitches as you fall asleep? This is nocturnal myoclonus, seen with remarkable frequency in patients who have PLMD. I also ask if the patient snores, if they have any irregular breathing, gasping, grunting or breath holding at night. It is important not to miss sleep apnea. Sleep apnea occurs not only in obese adults but is frequently missed in children who have sinus problems or large adenoids that obstruct their airways. It is important to know if there are any other sleep related problems. In particular enuresis and encopresis in children and adolescents. One hundred percent of the patients that I have seen through my practice who have had enuresis and/or encopresis have had a variety of prior treatments including Sudafed, Tofranil, and DDAVP Nasal Spray for bed-wetting in conjunction usually with painful psychotherapy to figure out the dynamic reason for the problem. The unfortunate individuals who have been embarrassed by encopresis have been further humiliated with diapers and remarks and psychotherapy that has attempted to find them victims of sexual abuse. The same one hundred percent of the patients who have been through my office have had complete resolution of their enuresis and/or encopresis with correction of their sleep disorder. Normalization of sleep architecture, usually with simple medicine such as Neurontin, solves the problem in these situations. Certainly there may be other patients with these difficulties for other reasons who will not respond to this treatment.

The presence of a tic disorder, simple or Tourette's Syndrome is important primarily in terms of the determination of proper treatment. Stimulants can unmask and exacerbate tics, an undesirable therapeutic result.

CONCENTRATION

How good is it? Does it vary with level of interest? Is the patient a daydreamer, easily distracted, impatient, impulsive, easily bored, easily frustrated, a procrastinator, one who worries a lot, tends to be moody? Does the patient hyperfocus, lock in on interesting things to the point that they are hard to interrupt or distract? Is there difficulty getting organized or started? Is there a tendency to have a variety of things going on at the same time with a tendency to jump from one to another without finishing?

HANDEDNESS

There is a remarkable incidence in the Neurosomatic Syndrome of left-handedness, mixed dominance, and right-handed people who were changed from being left-handed as children. This has some interesting implications for discussion of hemispheric dominance, learning issues, speech and language issues, and the like. I have some interesting anecdotal data which relates to the natural ability or difficulty with such things as foreign languages and mathematics dependent upon a child's handedness.

APPETITE

Has appetite been stable? Increased or decreased? In particular are there sugar and/or carbohydrate cravings? Again questions in this area may lead to disclosure of "bulimia" on the part of women and men. Many people often remark "doesn't everybody like sweets" when in fact this is not the case. Clearly there is a disorder of carbohydrate metabolism in the Neurosomatic Syndrome that has been identified as well in some depressive disorders, is present in virtually 100% of ADD people, and is very similar if not identical to the disorder of carbohydrate metabolism seen in Stein Leventhal Syndrome.

ANXIETY AND PANIC

What is the degree, duration, and experience of anxiety? Neurosomatic patients are worriers. They tend to be apprehensive, negativistic, and fear the worst. Some have panic attacks. The presence of frank panic attacks does not alter the diagnosis, or of necessity the treatment. In conjunction with queries about anxiety and panic is the determination of phobias. This does not include the routine snakes and spiders nor simple phobias such as heights or airplanes. Agoraphobia or multiple phobias occur in some cases and are consistent with the anxiety phobia syndrome which I believe is subsumed under the Neurosomatic Syndrome.

PSYCHOSIS

Hallucinations, delusions, persecutory ideation, referential ideation and the like are not part of the Neurosomatic Syndrome and take the examination in other directions. It is important to note however that many patients have been mislabeled as having hallucinations. People with severe anxiety and/or depression may hear voices inside their head. Hearing voices inside one's head is not by definition a psychotic manifestation but more often a symptom of anxiety and conscience. Additionally, and referable also to sleep, hallucinations that occur upon falling asleep or awakening (*hypnogogic and hypnopompic*) are not psychotic manifestations but manifestations of transitions into and out of sleep and may be symptomatic of narcolepsy.

COGNITIVE DYSFUNCTION

At one end of the spectrum is dementia. Dementia is not pertinent to the Neurosomatic Syndrome. Subtle forms of cognitive dysfunction and learning disability may be present in patients with the Neurosomatic Syndrome but are not cardinal symptoms thereof. The situation is more complex in patients with a history of head injury or epilepsy who may have a premorbid Neurosomatic Syndrome and/or a secondary mood/anxiety/attention/impulse problem from damage to the frontal lobes.

TICS

The presence of a tic disorder, simple or Tourette's Syndrome is important primarily in terms of the determination of proper treatment. Stimulants can unmask and exacerbate tics, an undesirable therapeutic result.

DIURNAL VARIATION

Diurnal variation means variation through the day. Of particular interest is to determine if the patient feels better or worse in the morning or evening. Does the day get better or does the day get worse? Neurosomatic patients tend to get better as the day wears on. They feel their most miserable and depressed and negativistic in the morning and may feel fairly upbeat in the evening. This is not true in all patients. When it is present it is often misdiagnosed as bipolar illness.

OBSESSIVE COMPULSIVE <u>SYMPTOMS</u>

Patients with the Neurosomatic Syndrome, particularly those with prominent attention deficit and anxiety symptoms frequently are misdiagnosed as having OCD--Obsessive Compulsive Disorder.

I shall explain the difference.

Patients with OCD have ego-dystonic symptoms. This is an old psychoanalytic term but it is correct. Intrusive obsessive thoughts come into the person's head over and over. The person is forced to think these thoughts over and over and over. The patient wishes the thoughts did not come. This is dystonic. (The opposite of ego dystonic is ego syntonic, something that is gratifying or soothing to the patient's ego). Similarly ego dystonic compulsions are present. The patient must engage in these compulsive behaviors and rituals over and over again in order to diminish some form of fear or anxiety or phobia but wishes dearly that he or she did not have to do these compulsive behaviors and rituals. This includes the gamut from counting to hand washing to preoccupations with germs to the need for absolute symmetry in organization to repacking the bureau or pantry or whatever a dozen times.

Patients with the Neurosomatic Syndrome frequently have obsessive compulsive symptoms. Very much "Type A" they think in a preoccupied or obsessive manner about things over and over. Because these people are thinking about several things at the same time, as if they were running five or ten computer programs simultaneously, they continue to circle through each and every one of them to monitor their status. Often because they have so much going on they become anxious and apprehensive as a result. This obsessional thinking actually has a calming effect because they then know the status of everything.

Patients with Neurosomatic obsessiveness often say that their mind races or won't turn off at night. Besides the intrinsic sleep disorder component of this syndrome they continue obsessively to review the day and go over and over and over all of the various things on their mind. This night time thinking pattern is misdiagnosed frequently as obsessive compulsive disorder or mania.

Compulsive-like but not ritualistic behaviors often are observed. The Neurosomatic patient with ADD symptoms develops a variety of compensatory strategies to deal with his or her disorganization and system overload. Hence they often will put things in the same place all the time so that they know where those things are and don't ever again have to spend time looking for their keys, wallet, purse, eyeglasses, lipstick, checkbook . . .

Neurosomatic patients with notable attentional symptoms also hyperfocus. They will lock in on a task or project to the point that it is hard to derail them or interrupt them. This is mistaken as a compulsive disorder. Besides the hyperfocus aspect these individuals often will finish tasks or assignments or projects immediately upon receipt of them with a self-knowledge that if they don't do it right now they'll put it off and lose it. Again these are obsessional and compulsive patterns that are adaptive and compensatory and for the most part ego syntonic.

MEDICAL HISTORY

Certainly it is important to know broadly and specifically the patient's medical history. This is necessary not just for diagnostic purposes but to make sure that treatment is appropriate and not improper given the patient's medical problems. From the Neurosomatic prospective several things must be unearthed. Often general questions such as " have you ever had any significant chronic or recurrent or acute medical problems or serious injuries?" are met with a shrug and negative answer. Therefore specific questioning is necessary. I will enquire if there is a history of fainting, seizures, diabetes, hypertension, liver disease, or cardiac disease. I will also enquire if there is a history of headaches and then follow up to determine exactly the kind, the quality, pattern and quantity of headaches. Patients frequently call mid-line, bitemporal, or behind the eyes headaches migraines. Truly these headaches have a migrainous quality but these are sleep disorder headaches. Migraine is almost always unilateral, on one side of the head. Thus many questions may be necessary to differentiate and delineate between the patient's headache and headache patterns. Many patients in fact have mid-line sleep disorder headaches, unilateral migraines of any form (common, classic, hemiplegic and so forth), and sinus headaches. Analgesic rebound may be commingled.

I then enquire if there is any history of stomach or gastrointestinal problems, ulcers, reflux esophagitis, colitis or irritable bowel syndrome. Yet again depending upon the pain threshold and stoicism of a patient they may have obvious patterns of irregular and irritable bowels or recurrent dyspepsia or heartburn but never have sought evaluation or treatment for it.

Enquiry is then made into sugar and/or carbohydrate cravings. At this point many patients disclose that they have had and may have had treatment for an "eating disorder". They call themselves bulimic. This is described above. Many patients also offer that they have TMJ syndrome and this is just a manifestation of their bruxism although again they may have had extensive evaluation and treatment and even multiple jaw surgeries.

Specific questions must be asked with female patients to determine if there's any evidence of premenstrual syndrome as it impacts mood, sleep, appetite, concentration, and have patterns.

Childhood ear infections, noted previously as prevalent in patients with ADHD similarly are present in Neurosomatic patients whether or not they have prominent attentional symptoms.

INJURIES

A remarkable number of patients have had multiple injuries, generally sports related orthopedic injuries although often traffic accidents and general falling down clumsiness is reported. Frequently they remark, "I'm a real Klutz!"

ALLERGIES

The prevalence of environmental allergies, hay fever, sinus trouble, and allergies to foods and dusts and a variety of substances is certainly over 90%. Medication allergies may be present but are much less. However Neurosomatic patients are quite atopic, allergic individuals. This will be discussed below with respect to histamine and other body chemistry. Asthma is very common.

FAMILY HISTORY

Family history is interesting and useful when it is present and accurate. However given the fact that much of what is described here has been ignored, maligned, and mismanaged for decades, it remains that many patients have no knowledge other than by their own observations of their family's Neuropsychiatric history.

PERSONAL HISTORY

Obviously questions are asked as to where the patient was born and raised, nature of family structure, history of trauma and abuse and so forth. Academic achievement and work history are pertinent questions to ask given the impact of attentional symptoms on the school performance and work performance of Neurosomatic patients. It's quite common to see a history in children and adolescents of gradually deteriorating school performance through transitions from grammar to middle school, middle school to high school and high school to college. It is common to see a history of poor work adjustment and frequent job changes in Neurosomatic patients.

Often obtained under school history, although sometimes

offered up under general medical history are admissions that the patient had a school phobia or used to get a lot of tummy aches as a child and in school and/or had lots of headaches and had to go home from school or stay home from school. These headaches, stomach upsets, vomiting, and anxiety symptoms are uniformly given a pejorative psychological interpretation and deemed to be attention seeking and/or avoidance mechanisms. In fact they are early manifestations of a Neurosomatic Syndrome.

DANGEROUSNESS

It is a necessity in a Neuropsychiatry examination always to enquire if a patient has had a history of thoughts of death, suicidal ideation, homicidal ideation or suicide attempts. These must be recorded and noted. I am not able to discern any difference in the incidence or prevalence of such experiences in Neurosomatic patients as compared to the general population.

DRUG AND ALCOHOL HISTORY

Neurosomatic patients have symptoms of anxiety, depression, insomnia, poor concentration, and pain. Self treatment with alcohol and marijuana is fairly common. It is also very common for these to be misdiagnosed as primary problems as opposed to secondary and self treatment problems.

The use or abuse of stimulants such as cocaine or amphetamine are very important. Neurosomatic patients who have tried such substances often say that they had a brief calming effect and that they felt very focused and clear. Subsequently they crash into depression. In the discussion of biogenic amine neurotransmitters that will follow in later chapters this will be explicated in detail with references to the work of some early researchers in this area.

PRIOR TREATMENT AND RESPONSE

This is an extremely broad and detailed category. The case histories illustrated below reveal a myriad of treatments both for the supposed medical as well as the supposed Neuropsychiatric aspects of this disorder. Those examples are self-evident. From the more traditional psychiatric perspective what is remarkable are the number of patients who have been treated with repeated courses of multiple SSRI's with bad effects only to end up miserable and on polypharmaceutical regimens. This mismanagement will be addressed in a substantial portion of the book to follow.

CHAPTER EIGHT
HISTORICAL NOTES AND ANECDOTES

In medicine anecdotes are personal observation and reports. Historically most of the major gains in medicine have been anecdotal. Someone noticed that a group of patients had similar complaints or characteristics and identified a syndrome or disease. Or an astute observation is made that bread mold kills bacteria and penicillin happens. Often these anecdotes led to eponyms: Steele-Richardson Syndrome and Stein-Leventhal Syndrome are examples.

Nowadays anecdotes often are sneered at. Only "scientific" data is acceptable, usually the type generated by an expensive study, funded by a drug company, upon which the reputation, tenure and future employment of the scientist is dependent, and for which a conclusion has been chosen that will be supported by the statistical data achieved in a placebo controlled double blinded study that is as unethical as it is unreliable. This attitude is inculcated in today's medical students and house officers who appear to spend far more time at computer terminals perusing diagnostic scenarios and treatment algorithms than examining patients and thinking. Along the way it became politically incorrect to honor a good doctor with an eponym, so the above referenced afflictions are now Progressive Supra-Nuclear Palsy (PSNP) and polycystic ovaries. Personally, I prefer the eponyms. I also prefer examining and thinking to not. Anecdotal observations in more than twenty years of practice led to this book. Many of these anecdotal observations are not mine but have been recorded for decades. Please consider the following.

1. A common symptom of eating disorders is depression.
2. A common symptom of depression is a sleep disorder.
3. A common symptom of a sleep disorder is depression.

4.   Depression, migraine and irritable bowel syndrome are often seen in the same patient.

5.   There is something awry in the HPA (*hypothalamic pituitary adrenal axis*) in patients with mood disorders.

6.   There seems to be some relationship between depression and high blood pressure (*hypertension*).

7.   Patients with chronic complaints of insomnia or poor sleep also complain a lot about headaches, generalized aches and pains, and often don't get better.

8.   Anxious patients seem to have a lot of physical complaints.

9.   Patients with a lot of unsatisfactorily treated physical complaints are often quite anxious.

10. Patients with Attention Deficit Hyperactivity Disorder seem to have a high incidence of sleep, anxiety and mood problems.

COMMON SLUR: These are annoying, hard to deal with patients who are never satisfied and aren't really very sick because they have a bunch of stress related psychosomatic/psychophysiologic disorders which reflect poorly on their character and/or their upbringing. Ever since hypochondriasis became a politically incorrect term such patients are now typically labeled by the newer, more precise and politically correct term CROCKS.

Two nuclei identified in the hypothalamus, the ventral-median and the ventral-lateral have been identified as having something to do with appetite. Damage to the former causes hyperphagia, continuous eating because of an inability to experience satiety. Damage to the latter stops eating because of an inability to experience hunger. Both are fatal.

Hormones are chemical messengers produced by endocrine glands, and are carried through the blood stream to the target organ. That may be another gland or not. The existence of such substances was first suggested by Sigmund Freud in his _THREE ESSAYS ON SEXUALITY_ written in 1905.

CHAPTER NINE
CASE EXAMPLES

CASEY

Casey is a twelve year old girl in the sixth grade, her first year of middle school. It has not been a good year.

Heretofore Casey had been a good student in the primary grades. She was quiet, apparently attentive and polite. She had participated in class, got her work done and got good grades. Then some changes occurred.

Casey began sixth grade at the middle school. The summer before her menarche occurred and she began to have menstrual periods and typical body changes. Her school performance plummeted and she began to fail courses, have behavior problems and temper problems. She would be angry, moody and sullen. Belligerent and obnoxious were words frequently used to describe her.

Since everyone already knew that Casey was a bright girl as demonstrated by her prior performance and school testing she was accused of being oppositional, lazy, indifferent and stoned. Temper tantrums occurred at home and at school.

Uncertain what was going on the parents took Casey to her pediatrician. They did a drug screen which was negative and accepted that drug abuse was not a present concern. The pediatrician recommended a counselor who saw the patient once and said that Casey was Bipolar. A nurse practitioner working with the counselor began Casey on Paxil. This seemed to calm her for about a week or two but then she became agitated again and every two to three weeks the Paxil was increased up to a total daily dose of 60 mg. Again after a few weeks on a 60 mg dose Casey became irritable and belligerent and had Depakote added to her regimen. As

41

a result she became lethargic and tractable, if indifferent and detached. Her school performance improved insofar as she was no longer a behavior problem. She just sat there often staring off into space. Her grades did not improve but her behavior was contained.

Over a period of some two months Casey gained about twenty pounds, her menses ceased, and she began to get some facial and body hair which she did not like. Casey had never been a great sleeper. She'd always had some headaches and had begun to have what were believed to be migraines with her menstrual period. These seemed to get worse and worse during the year. Mom called the pediatrician who recommended a neurological consultation and Casey was seen by a neurologist.

The neurologist accepted the diagnosis of a Bipolar Disorder made by the counselor and nurse practitioner and focused directly on the migraine. The neurologist thought that Prozac would be better for Casey's migraine than Paxil and recommended a change. The neurologist had heard something about a need to taper the Paxil so it was recommended that Casey take 40 mg of Paxil for one day, 20 mg the next day and then stop it as she began to take Prozac 20 mg every day. Mom and Casey followed the recommendations diligently and within 48 hours Casey was berserk. She was screaming and crying and scratching herself and said she wanted to crawl out of her skin and couldn't sleep and was smashing things and breaking things about the house. She lost control at school and the police were summoned and arrested Casey and took her to juvenile hall.

ALLAN

Allan, thirty-nine, has a problem with headaches, both his and others, insofar as his chronic and persistent headache complaints, coupled with their refractory response to a multitude of treatments have induced a similar condition in a dozen or so specialists and consultants not to mention the odd chiropractor, acupuncturist and aroma therapist seen along the way. To say that Allan has headaches is to say that the Sahara has sand. Allan has headaches of great variety and texture, quality and intensity. Diagnoses notwithstanding, the final common feature of them all is that nothing much seems to help. His head hurts so badly and so often that once, when a frustrated intern remarked that the best way to stop the headaches would be to slam his fingers in a drawer, Allan almost gave it a try before he gave it a second thought and decided that, if the opportunity presented itself, he'd slam the intern's fingers somewhere instead.

For Allan, the moments that his head does not hurt are memorable, almost epiphany. In the morning he awakens with a headache, usually a dense boring pain right through the center of his forehead and around and through his eyes. It's a searing deep pain that aches indescribably. Later, after some coffee and a hand full of pills it wanes a bit, only until he sees some wavy lines and dancing spots in his left eye and it's only a matter of seconds until the sharp, lancinating pain burns and throbs through his temple and eye and light and sound and touch are unbearable and nausea is a relief and it feels like a sadistic dentist is at work in his cranium with a blowtorch and a soldering iron. His face droops, his eyes don't focus, his teeth don't seem to fit. After a while the pain diminishes and he feels just lousy. Which is a relief until the pain builds and throbs in his temples and the back of his head and neck are in a vise and he can't move without feeling it jar so bad he wishes his head would fall off and roll away and fall down a deep hole somewhere like the miserable eight ball it is.

Diagnoses abound: migraine; cluster; tension, sinus, neurosis, TMJ! Treatments collide and Allan stumbles from doctor to chiropractor to pain clinic to therapist to yoga to bed and has an overall cruddy time. Over the years he's been on over 50 different drugs, usually on at least 5 or 6 at a time. His present regimen includes Elavil at bedtime causing constipation, dry mouth, blurred vision and almost enough misery to counter the headaches; Calan XL a calcium channel blocking heart/blood pressure pill that is sometimes prophylactic for migraine; Zoloft 200 mg each day, an SSRI. On it he has no libido and no orgasms and is more tense and restless than ever; three Imitrex injections almost daily. These are fast acting vasoconstrictors which can cause strokes and heart attacks; Stadol nasal spray too often an addictive narcotic that works briefly and wears off; Advil a lot, too often; Zantac, an H2 blocker because the Advil rips up his stomach; Restoril for sleep. Not much, but now he can't do without it.

MAUREEN

At fifty-nine Maureen thought things should be better. Healthy grown children, healthy grandchildren, healthy retired husband, reasonable security, no bad diseases herself except that she just feels awful all of the time. No energy. No stamina, no desire. Depressed, well yes a bit, but mostly about feeling so lousy and being a stick in the mud when everyone else seems so busy with life. Sleep is a problem. She's always tired. And she awakens in such pain, particularly around the neck and shoulders and down her back and her arms and legs feel like they weigh a ton and then she gets these throbbing miserable headaches and feels pain . . .

Maureen had had some problems throughout her life. As a teenager and young adult she'd had some periods of anxiety or lightheadedness and panicky feelings. She'd been told then that she was hypoglycemic and placed on a diet of complex carbohydrates in several small feedings per day. This problem seemed to go away for a while but then reemerged in her thirties. The new doctor she saw determined that she had Chronic Fatigue Syndrome. Exactly what that is or was was never understood by Maureen. She took vitamins and tried acupuncture but the things that seemed to help the most were vacations.

In her forties symptoms recurred and Maureen was referred to a psychiatrist who said she had Panic Disorder. They tried a little of this and a little of that until finally she was begun on Prozac. Her panic seemed to diminish but for years she has been rather blah and bland and apathetic and her sleep, never terrific, has become worse.

The doctors tried a variety of regimens. But then they decided that she had Fibromyalgia, or a Myofascial Pain Syndrome, but couldn't explain what it was to her satisfaction and she is not a stupid person. Once having made the diagnosis they again tried some of this and some of that which at the present time is Prozac 40 mg every morning, Elavil 25-50 mg every night, Ambien 5 mg every night and Advil whenever Maureen wants to take it.

TIFFANY

Tiffany is a very unhappy thirty four year old woman. She has a serious weight problem. Her therapist says it's Bulimia. Tiffany binge eats. Sometimes she purges, too, not out of guilt, but because she feels that if she doesn't, she'll explode. This has been going on since adolescence. She does not have Anorexia Nervosa. She never thought she was too fat when she wasn't, or exercised compulsively, or restricted calories. She doesn't binge everyday, nor in any particular pattern or cycle, but several times a week, and sometimes several times a day, she just gorges herself. This will often happen in the late afternoon, or in the late hours of the night. Bags of Oreo's, candy bars, sweet rolls and such like are consumed at a frightening rate. Quite clearly she craves sugar, plain and simple sugar. Not protein, not fat, just sugar. Sometimes it is sugar, as in cubes of!

She's tried every conceivable diet and program, including O.A., and sometimes lost weight, only to put it right back on again. A fat doctor once gave her Dexedrine and it worked great and she felt fine and normal and not high and he lost his license. She tried Redux and Phen Phen briefly, but didn't feel right, and quit before they were withdrawn because a woman she knew in O.A., named Estelle, died of pulmonary hypertension.

No one, including the HMO psychiatrist who prescribes her present regimen knows, because no one has ever asked, that Tiffany has always been rather anxious and moody, and seems to be okay for a while and then have a moment often just a few hours in an afternoon when she feels really good and positive and hopeful and then she sort of crashes and feels lousy and miserable and worthless, and that she's never been a good sleeper, never seemed to need much, but is always tired in the morning, and that she was an adequate student who found school a bore and tended to tune out and daydream a lot and leave assignments until the last minute and then rush to do them and was told she wasn't working up to her potential and was lazy.

Coincidentally her psychiatrist and her therapist have echoed the same theme and suggested that she really doesn't want to get better and isn't trying hard enough because she's on the proper treatment regimen and the rest is up to her. Tiffany feels hopeless and at times contemplates suicide because now with the proper treatment, she still binges and cycles and doesn't sleep well and her weight which used to fluctuate between 140# and 190# is now at 230# and rising and she has lost all interest in sex and can no longer climax anyhow and her husband has about had it and when she has tried to stop her medicine she literally thinks she will go crazy and crawl out of her skin and can't stop crying and is chastised by her HMO psychiatrist who smugly points out that it is abundantly obvious that Tiffany cannot survive without the proper medication which at the present time appears to be Paxil 60 mg per day for her eating disorder and Trazadone 150 mg a night for her sleep and Depakote 250 mg three times a day to help her control her impulses.

Her persistent complaints of cramps, flatus, and alternating diarrhea and constipation are attributed to her eating problem. It was once described as possible Irritable Bowel Syndrome but again was an obvious concomitant of her eating problem and would probably go away if she just took better control of her impulses and her oral needs and grew up and stopped all this nonsense.

LEONARD

Oy! Leonard. What a kvetch! If its not one thing its another. His head, his nerves, his belly, his nerves, his bowels, his nerves, his head, his nerves, his rectum, his nerves, his esophagus, his nerves, his sleep, his nerves, his cramps, his nerves, his gas, his nerves, his diarrhea, his nerves.

Leonard is a challenge. His knowledge of anatomy, his eloquent graphic descriptions of a malfunction, his lugubrious exposition to anyone anytime of his travail can irritate inanimate objects.

However, it is true that Leonard is a wretch. A good old-fashioned nervous wreck. He does not have phobias or panic attacks. He has good old-fashioned anxiety, an abundance of it. Though he does have the occasional migraine headache, and he doesn't sleep well, mostly Leonard has a problem with his alimentary canal, all of it, start to finish.

From the top down first is the reflux esophagitis (GERD) this leads to the gastritis and peptic ulcer symptoms. He has not had a gastric ulcer, and he is H.Pylori negative, but he has had a duodenal ulcer. He doesn't have Crohn's Disease (the eponym that preceded regional ileitis), nor ulcerative colitis. There is some diverticulitis and rip-roaring irritable bowel syndrome (IBS).

There are the constant cramps; alternate diarrhea and constipation – with attendant hemorrhoids – nausea, burning, belching (eructation), belly noises (borborygmi), and at the end of the day, flatus. Of course all the tests and studies have been done; negative. Ever since childhood when Leonard was a tense and nervous boy he would ruminate apprehensively about everything; worry, worry, worry. He would perspire, get a tummy ache, often throw up, and always be distressed; about a ball game, about school, a party, you name it. Whatever happened, or might, he worried about it. This led his first three therapists to label him as anal retentive. Whatever the case the psychotherapies helped as much as the many somatic therapies – not very much.

Leonard has been on a vast number of medications. At present he takes Levsinex time caps, to slow his bowel and diminish pain and cramps; Prevacid to block the release of hydrochloric acid in his stomach, Axid a histamine 2 blocker, antacids by the pint, Fiorinal with Codeine as needed for his migraine headaches, Halcion for sleep, and Procardia a calcium channel blocker for hypertension.

GINA

For most of her twenty six years Gina has been anxious. Or more to the point, a nervous wreck. Panic is her life. Fear is her constant companion. She's sure that she has invented phobias; heights, open spaces, closed spaces, elevators, highways, bridges, airplanes. Even to shop is a problem!

Her mother says that she was a nervous finicky baby who startled easily. Her teenage brother says she's a wuss. Her former therapist vehemently insisted that Gina was a victim of incest and had repressed memories of it that the therapist would certainly find in time, perhaps along with several other personalities in this and previous lives. Lucky for Gina the therapist joined a cult before any more harm was done.

It happened suddenly, once upon a time, for no apparent reason. She felt a little faint; her heart began to race and pound and palpitate and her chest hurt and she couldn't seem to breathe and her face and fingers tingled and everything closed in on her and doom was imminent and the terror incredible. And that was just the start!

None of the treatments worked. They seemed promising at first but all seemed to lose their initial benefit in a short time. Not Paxil or Prozac or Zoloft or Serzone, nor Norpramin or Aventyl or Buspar or Depakote or Xanax and Klonopin or Whiskey or Rye. Why couldn't she be like some of the other people in the agoraphobia group. They all had panic disorder and most were depressed like her. Why were others so fine on Prozac today and why did some do so well on Wellbutrin. And others took a little bit of Valium. What gives? Gina's present regimen includes Tegretol 200 mg three times a day *a mood stabilizer,* Serzone 200 mg twice a day *an anti anxiety antidepressant,* Luvox 150 mg twice a day *an SSRI,* Risperdal 2 mg twice a day *a major tranquilizer/anti-psychotic,* Buspar 30 mg twice a day *a novel anxiolytic.*

MARY

Hopeless, helpless, worthless, useless, bad, no good, ought to be dead; this summarizes Mary's thoughts and feelings all day and all night day in and day out for what has seemed to be an eternity. To say that she suffers from depression does not do justice to the depth of her despair, her misery, her pain. Sleep comes but rarely and when it does it is shallow and fitful and full of nightmares. To look forward with eager anticipation, to experience joy or laughter, to want to do something, anything but disappear and die are as incomprehensible to her as Sanskrit.

This has nothing to do with her childhood, her toilet training, her diet or her Karma. This is a disease, a very bad disease, called depression. It is nasty and painful and crippling and often fatal. And all too often it is treated very poorly and the vulnerable suffering patient is told that they aren't trying hard enough or that they don't really want to get better.

Poor Mary has tried everything. Rolfing and praying and primal screaming and analyzing and modeling and twelve stepping and hypnotic regression and acupuncture and herbs and spices and voodoo and medications up the wahzoo and finally suicide; an overdose of the herbs and spices and medications and vodka and Draino. Naturally her therapist told her that she wasn't trying hard enough and didn't want really to get better and her family was angry with her and her minister coldly admonished her for her lack of faith and devotion – all very helpful when she was intubated in the intensive care unit (ICU) unable to respond and feeling like guano. Besides the various and sundry psychotherapies Mary's treatment has included, singly and in incredible combination: Elavil, Tofranil, Aventyl, Surmontil, Sinequan, Vivactyl, Paxil, Prozac; Zoloft, Luvox, Lithium, Depakote, Tegretol, Cytomel, Remeron, Soma, Flexeril, Nardil, Xanax, Librium, Miltown, Stellazine, Mellaril, Navane, Risperdal, and several other sedatives, and so forth and so on.

This list does not include the other medication that Mary has been treated with for chronic migraine, recurrent ulcers and irritable bowels, and her blood pressure.

Mary is thirty-three years old. Her present specialist has recommended electroconvulsive therapy (ECT) to treat her refractory depression. Mary, who believes that she has lost her mind anyhow is prepared to go ahead and get buzzed, whether she needs it or not.

BERT

Bert is a 52 year old business man with an occult eating disorder. It's occult insofar as he's kept it secret most of his life and was reluctant to disclose it and reticent to speak of it ever since he made an off hand remark to a physician friend. He'd casually inquired if the physician knew of men having eating disorders and the physician, an internist, said he wasn't terribly familiar with it but as far as he knew men with eating disorders were all homosexual. This troubled Bert greatly and he didn't mention it again to anyone else except his wife.

Bert had had some sort of stomach trouble since childhood. Frequent tummy aches kept him home from school. He seemed to have a sensitive stomach and would throw up rather easily. Throughout his life he had on and off trouble with migraine, and a significant degree of anxiety with mild high blood pressure.

Curiously Bert had always been a very poor sleeper. As a small child he simply never wanted to go to bed and wanted to stay up reading or watching television. By the time he was eight or nine his parents finally gave up and went to bed and allowed Bert to stay downstairs and watch the Jack Paar show until the television station went off the air. Then Bert would read a little while, go to bed for what amounted to a modest nap, and get up at five or so and read until the TV station was turned on again and he would watch the Today Show with Dave Garroway.

Bert always seemed to favor carbohydrates. An entire bag of potato chips could disappear in no time. He always seemed to reach for something that was sugary or had a lot of starch in it. By the

51

time he was in college Bert found that he would often overeat to the point that he would feel bloated, become sick to his stomach and then have to throw up. The vomiting was not a desirable event and had nothing to do with concerns about his weight or body image but simply because he felt so miserable from having eaten so much that he had to empty it out lest he explode. At those times he would feel incredibly tense and anxious perspiring and have marked abdominal cramps.

Bert has had the usual thorough bowel run, examined and endoscoped from stem to stern with no abnormalities discerned. Working with his latest physician he's talked around the subject a little bit. His problems remain pretty much the same. His latest regimen includes Hydrochlothyazide for blood pressure; Librax for cramps, and Sonata for sleep.

CRAIG

Craig is approaching forty. He's been married, divorced and remarried. His job as a software engineer in a start-up company is quite pressured. When asked what he wanted for his fortieth birthday his reply was "a good night's sleep". Craig's really never been sick. He's had some minor annoyances from time to time which he's ignored in a stoic and manly way. He gets headaches and takes Tylenol. He gets cramps or diarrhea and takes some Lomotil and Metamucil. For the past four or five years he has taken a dose of Vasotec daily for his blood pressure.

He's never seen himself as depressed or terribly anxious but rather as an intense and driven individual. He's always had multiple projects going on at the same time and generally been able to handle them in a reasonably efficient manner.

Craig never thought much about his sleep until he realized that he was exhausted. When questioned carefully his history revealed that his sleep had always been rather poor and light and fitful but never seemed to bother him until he was about thirty-five or thirty-six. By the time he was thirty-seven he was taking over the counter sleeping pills and washing them down with a stiff nightcap. By the time he was thirty-eight he began to see doctors about his problems with sleep.

He heard all of the usual things about pacing himself and taking time and getting some rest. He had a sleep study that did not find sleep apnea. It was read as essentially normal. The individual who read the study remarked that Craig spent very little time in deep sleep, had prolonged REM latencies (it took a long time before he began to dream and he didn't dream very much) and that there was a lot of alpha intrusion into his deep sleep. He said that this pattern was often read in people who were tense and anxious. Craig has become incredibly preoccupied with his sleep. He feels exhausted most of the time. He's aware that he's been grinding his teeth and has chewed through bite blocks. At this point he takes Trazadone 150 mg plus Remeron 15 mg plus Sonata 10 mg plus a gin and tonic, two large glasses every night before bed.

LASZLO

Laszlo is a fifty-six year old businessman. Bright, incredibly hard working, a quick study are some of the words that have been used to describe to him. Other words have included brusque, intrusive and obnoxious. He tends to finish other people's sentences and zoom right along. Never one for tedious bureaucracy and meetings and routine for its own sake, Laszlo's stepped on a lot of toes and egos and rubbed people the wrong way and hasn't fit in really well and done his own thing and found that he's never been a group kind of a guy and hasn't often been invited into the fraternity or club or inner circle or what have you, at least not for long, or only if they really want something from him. Readily bored, easily frustrated, often finding his daydreams far more interesting than pedestrian conversation, Laszlo loses interest swiftly in mundane discourse. Laszlo always needs to be busy. He'll have several things going on at once. However he seems to wait until the last minute to get things done, a trait that has perturbed teachers, partners, bosses and his wife on a continuous basis. Stubborn, intense and stoic Laszlo has never made much of his intermittent headaches, recurrent stomach trouble and such like. If necessary some over the counter medicaments provided a bit of relief. Being a poor sleeper who never seemed to need very much anyhow never bothered him until his wife finally refused to sleep in the same bed with him because he rolled and jumped and kicked around so much that she couldn't sleep at all, and she didn't want her nose broken, again, by his flailing about!

JEROME

A nervous fellow always, Jerome had a panic attack at his first wedding (Jerome is a Unitarian clergyman). The scene on the alter was, well, unusual.

Jerome had always been somewhat delicate. He had a delicate stomach and was prone to headaches. He was "highly strung" and a light sleeper. He seemed continuously to worry and ruminate about one thing or another and his blood pressure was always at best borderline high to hypertensive. Jerome went frequently to the doctor.

Begun first on Zoloft he immediately felt as if he was going to crawl out of his skin. His psychiatrist switched him immediately to Wellbutrin SR 150 mg twice daily and Jerome did well.

When last he saw his family physician it was noted that his migraine headaches had diminished, his blood pressure was low so his blood pressure medicine was stopped, and his bowels had settled down. He still had problems falling asleep and remained a light and fitful sleeper and wanted to know if he had a TMJ problem and should see an oral surgeon.

FRANK

Frank is a fifty-eight year old attorney. He has always seemed driven. Type A, a hard worker, a workaholic. Also a stoic, tough guy. He's never paid attention to little aches and pains. He never cared whether he slept well and heartburn never bothered him. His blood pressure was elevated a bit but he didn't like to have to remember to take medication.

Too much denial is not a good thing. Frank didn't pay attention to some of those chest pains he was getting until he got a really crushing one and ended up in the emergency room with a heart attack. He had an angiogram and an agioplasty and eventually coronary artery bypass graft surgery on four blood vessels. He weathered this all very well.

But his recovery was slow and tedious and soon to be held back by a lack of enthusiasm and no energy and no interest and apathy and grumpiness and blue mood and what everybody and the doctors and his relatives said was depression. Frank of course denied that he was depressed but then Frank never was one for feelings.

The cardiologist put him on Zoloft which Frank didn't like because it made him jumpy and impotent. So the family doctor tried Paxil. This was worse and Frank became belligerent. A psychiatrist put Frank on Prozac which initially seemed to mellow him out but now mostly seems to have wiped him out. To say that Frank is blasé would be to minimize. Frank is there but not entirely. He just sits and drifts and doesn't much care.

BETTY

Betty, in her twenties, has had headaches since childhood. They kept her home from school. When she was little she would complain of a headache and get to stay home. She had tummy aches from time to time but more often they were headaches. Often she would awaken in the morning with a headache and be rubbing her forehead and crying and unhappy.

As a small child it was difficult for the doctors to understand exactly what hurt. She could not be very precise in describing the quality of the pain, the nature of the pain, the intensity of the pain or the precise location. She had a headache.

As Betty got older she could be more articulate and precise in the description of her distress. Her whole head hurt. There didn't seem to be a starting point or focus. The pain would be through her forehead and temples and behind and between her eyes and through the back of her head and around her head and down her neck.

The quality of the pain. It hurt. It throbbed and ached and often pulsed and sometimes felt like there was hot needle shooting through one eye or the other. Occasionally there would be some nausea but not too often.

Betty experienced increasing amounts of pain in her temples and jaw. Her dentist told her that she clearly had TMJ and ground her teeth a lot. He fashioned for her a dental apparatus to wear at night that cost her about $200.00. This enabled her to grind the apparatus instead of her teeth. Her temples and jaw still hurt. The dentist said that X Rays of her TMJ (temporal mandibular joints) didn't show anything amiss but he wanted her to go see a TMJ specialist who could operate on her jaw joints and may be give her some relief.

Betty's sleep is poor. She has difficulty falling asleep, she wakes frequently and is a very light sleeper. She tends to flop around a bit and as a result is not a comfortable bed partner. She's been told that her headaches and jaw pain are causing her to have poor quality sleep. She doesn't dream much anymore and in fact can't recollect the last time she really had a dream. She does day dream though and that's usually about having her headaches go away and getting a good night sleep.

Her present treatment, besides her bite block includes Trazadone for sleep which makes her feel very groggy in the morning; Motrin in high doses for her pain supplemented with Fiorinal and sometimes with Vicodan. Prozac was started to try and stop the headaches. It seemed to have a brief positive effect which lasted for a few weeks but then led to an increase in dose with a positive effect for a few weeks and this pattern continued until she achieved a dose of 60 mg per day which she has been on for six months. The Prozac doesn't seem to help the headaches very much and Betty's sleep seems to be worse. Her jaw still hurts. She's gained about thirty pounds and has completely lost her libido. This has not helped her marriage, her self-image or her self-esteem very much.

Betty's quite frustrated by the whole thing. She's had all the tests the doctors can think of. Since childhood she's had sinus X Rays, been given eyeglasses, had allergy shots. You name it, she's had it. And she has had it. Especially since the counselor at the pain management program to which she had been referred told her that she must not really want to get better.

RACHAEL

Rachael is a twenty eight year old ambivalently married female. Rachael is perplexed. Rachael has not had notable difficulties throughout her early life and adolescence. She was a satisfactory student with no health problems. She didn't do drugs. She finished college at age twenty two with a Bachelor's Degree in Anthropology. At that point she was not sure what to do with her life and felt somewhat anxious and disconnected. She was apprehensive about the future. Graduate school or a job were before her.

During a routine office visit with her family physician to assess and treat a bladder infection Rachael mentioned that she was somewhat anxious and unhappy. The well intentioned family doctor asked a few questions during the ten minute visit and decided that Rachael was depressed. He recommended Zoloft. Rachael began Zoloft initially at a 25 mg dose. As luck would have it Rachael felt an initial calming and detachment but this was not long lived. It would seem that the medicine would work for a few weeks or a month and then Rachael would become anxious and somewhat unhappy and she would call the doctor and the dose would be increased. Ultimately at a dose of 150 mg per day Rachael no longer felt anxious or distressed. In actuality Rachael felt very little at this point. Things didn't bother her and she was able to go about life without being too concerned about much of anything. Rachael worked for awhile and then decided to go to graduate school in business administration. By the time she was twenty six Rachael had an MBA and a good job with a growing company.

Rachael met a man at work who found her quite attractive. After dating for awhile Rachael agreed to marry the man. She didn't seem to have really strong feelings but thought it was the right time to do this.

Two years into the marriage Rachael had some feelings of anxiety and uncertainty. There had also been some discussion of children and she didn't know what to do with her Zoloft.

Seen by a psychiatrist the history was reviewed and no clear evidence to support the diagnosis of a biological mood or anxiety disorder could be established. With care Rachael was detoxified from the Zoloft over a period of four weeks. This occurred without distress. Over the next month or so Rachael began to have feelings again. Some of them were unpleasant feelings of anxiety and apprehension and frustration and ambivalence that she had experienced earlier. She was now also able to experience joy and pleasure and eager anticipation.

Rachael agreed with the psychiatrist's assessment that the Zoloft hadn't been indicated in the first place and that it had suppressed her feelings for a long time. Now, six years later Rachael had to deal with the issues that she hadn't dealt with at age twenty two and learn to handle herself and her emotions as an adult in the adult world. Problematic for Rachael was now that she was effectively sober she was horrified to find herself married. Her husband was a nice fellow but she had no strong feelings for him and couldn't understand why she had done a lot of what she had done over the past six years.

This did little to comfort Rachael's husband who was furious at Rachael and at the psychiatrist who had simply assessed her and detoxified her from Zoloft

ROBERT

Robert is a 43 year old professional. He learned a long time ago to describe himself as a Type A personality, this an excuse or rationalization for his way of being. Driven and hard working his list of problems includes hypertension; peptic ulcer disease with gastroesophageal reflux disease (PUD w/GERD); chronic insomnia characterized by difficult falling asleep, poor quality sleep with frequent wakenings, and awakening tired, often with a headache. He grinds his teeth (bruxism) and often kicks around a lot a night and has place kicked his wife several times. He has chronic muscle tension headaches with some mixed vascular (migrainous) component. He worries constantly and seems unreasonably anxious. His bowels are "irregular". Though none of his specialists bothered to ask it turns out that as a child he used to get very anxious about tests and the like and got frequent tummy aches, often to the point of vomiting. His eating habits are poor.

Over the years Robert has seen a variety of specialists. At present, despite managed care, he has an internist, a gastroenterologist, a neurologist, and a large pharmacy bill every month. He has been resistant to referral to a psychiatrist because he resents any inference that he needs one. He did see a therapist once for "stress management" but quit after two sessions having no interest in finding his inner child or trying to recall his toilet training travails.

His present regimen includes Vasotec *an angiotensin converting enzyme inhibitor (ACE Inhibitor)* Tenormin, *a beta blocker both for his blood pressure;* Prilosec, *inhibits acid secretion and* Pepcid, *a histamine 2 or H2 blocker* and antacids as needed. He takes Metamucil for his irregularity; Ambien for sleep *which isn't supposed to be habit forming but is,* often supplemented by a night cap; and Fiorinal and/or Darvocet-N 100 for moderate headaches with a shot or pill of Imitrex for severe headaches. In addition his medicine chest contains Flexeril *a muscle relaxant* for aches, pains and general tension with Buspar for anxiety (this never worked well so he doesn't take it and he prefers wine at lunch and dinner) and finally a custom made bite block which he gagged on when he found he could get just about the same thing at a sporting good store for 99¢.

WHITNEY

IT **IS** ALL IN YOUR HEAD:
A Monograph on Wellness for the New Millennium

Whitney is fourteen. She had always been a quiet and polite little girl who seemed to pay attention and did reasonably well. She would sit in her chair, not fidget or be disruptive and daydream quietly. She was lost in her thoughts and fantasies that were far more interesting than the redundant classroom discussions around her.

Whitney breezed through the primary grades. In middle school she went from a straight A student to a B-C student. Her testing showed that she was quite bright and she and her parents were told that she basically was lazy and not working up to her potential.

As Whitney went through the changes in puberty and menarche she developed some abdominal pains that were rather vague and it wasn't clear to the pediatrician if she was having menstrual or bowel problems or both. She was progressively tired and irritable. She had difficulty falling asleep and when she finally did she had terrible problems getting up in the morning and was fussy and grouchy and often unpleasant. Temper tantrums and anger outbursts began to manifest and fireworks between Whitney and her mother were becoming nearly daily events. Whitney's pediatrician wasn't quite sure what to make of all of this. He referred Whitney to a therapist. The therapist thought that Whitney's anger was a manifestation of depression and recommended Paxil to the pediatrician. The pediatrician agreed and put Whitney on Paxil and initially she was a bit mellowed out but this seemed to last only a couple of weeks and the dose was increased. This pattern occurred until Whitney was taking 60 mg of Paxil. She seemed at times rather detached but at other times was quite moody. The therapist was now convinced that Whitney was Bipolar (manic depressive) and told the pediatrician that a mood stabilizer would be necessary. The pediatrician was not comfortable with this and referred Whitney and her mother to a psychiatrist who saw Whitney for twenty minutes and agreed with the therapist that Whitney was Bipolar and began a course a Depakote.

Whitney is under control. She hasn't been having outbursts. Her school performance remains dreadful. She is rather indifferent. Her sleep didn't improve and so Trazadone was added. Over a period of eight months Whitney's menses have ceased, she has gained thirty pounds, and is beginning to grow an unusual amount of facial and body hair.

WALLACE

Anxiety attacks plagued Wallace for years. Unfortunately he didn't know what they were. He always felt better after a few drinks. He had insufferable side effects from innumerable medications: Paxil and Zoloft and Norpramin, etc. He didn't have side effects from several other drugs, which was a very good thing. Except they didn't work very well, either.

Wallace had other problems along the way. All were attributed to his being so nervous, so high-strung. Hence he had a nervous stomach and a nervous bowel and nervous tension headaches and nervous migraine headaches and nervous insomnia and nervous mild high blood pressure ("Wally, you're just too tense, too uptight, you need to settle down," said one doctor).

Multiple drug trials – all of the above and several more – convinced Wallace that either he or the doctors were crazy. If he weren't so anxious or so miserable from side effects he could be more clear about the conclusion. Not just psychotropic drugs, Wallace had been on a variety of multi drug regimens for the aforementioned afflictions, the benefit rarely worth the side effects. Psychotherapy was of equal utility.

Until a curmudgeon of a psychiatrist, who got writer's cramp trying to record Wallace's history pulled him off of everything, brought him back in two weeks drug free – and with all of the noted complaints on the rise – put him on Valium 5 mg twice a day, brought him back in two more weeks – symptom free – and told him to go live his life in peace.

INEZ

Inez is a nice woman. Mid thirties, college graduate, mother of two, pursues her career in business as she takes care of her family. Hardly a day goes by when she doesn't have trouble with her stomach, or her bowels, or her belly. This isn't new. In fact its an old story. Inez had some colic as a baby. As a toddler she had trouble with constipation and going to the bathroom. Throughout her childhood and adolescence she was plagued by bellyaches, cramps, diarrhea, gas, burning, distention, nausea, and sometimes vomiting.

Inez has been evaluated thoroughly. She's had upper and lower GI series. She's had a gastroscopy and a colonoscopy. She's had a CT Scan of her abdomen. She's even had a laparoscopy to rule out the possibility of endometriosis, a gynecological problem, as the source of her difficulties. Her most recent consultant has recommended that she see a surgeon to have a laparotomy, a procedure wherein her entire abdomen is opened and explored visually and physically by a surgeon to discern if there is any abnormality.

Throughout the years Inez has been said to have lactose intolerance, gluten intolerance, sugar and refined flour intolerance, allergies, and abdominal migraine. It has been ascertained that she doesn't have a problem with her gallbladder or her pancreas or her liver or her kidneys or her female reproductive organs. She has a problem with her bowels. Irritable bowel syndrome.

IT **IS** ALL IN YOUR HEAD:
A Monograph on Wellness for the New Millennium

She has tried all of the diets, high fiber and low fiber, high protein low protein, high fat no fat, macrobiotic, vegetarian . . . Nothing really seems to help.

Certainly she's heard that she has a "functional" problem. Yes she's a nervous person. Yes she's had a tendency to panic attacks from time to time. She's moody. She does get classic migraine headaches and also these annoying between the eyes middle of the forehead headaches that plague her randomly throughout the day, but mostly its her bowels. If they would just settle down she could live a normal happy life. As it is she can't feel secure in the car for more than twenty minutes.

Inez has tried remedies old and new. Paxil gave her immediate cramps and diarrhea besides terrible insomnia. At present she takes Donnatal four times a day in conjunction with bran, and Darvocet for severe cramps. She has a variety of pills for her headaches and anxiety which include Fioricet, Immitrex, Naprosyn, Skelaxin, and Amitriptyline.

HAROLD

Harold is six. He's had a variety of difficulties throughout his life. He'd always been perceived as a rather anxious and timid child, clinging to mom. He had frequent complaints of tummy aches and headaches and had been seen many times by his pediatrician and consultants with no clear diagnosis made other than he seemed to be anxious. When it came time to go to school Harold had difficulty going. He would cry and scream and not want his mother to leave. Harold was sent to a therapist.

The therapist diagnosed Harold with a school phobia, separation anxiety, social anxiety, panic disorder, and probable obsessive-compulsive disorder. The latter diagnosis was based upon mother's description of Harold's room. Harold liked his toys to be

64

in certain places and would get upset if somebody moved them. The therapist recommended Zoloft and Harold at age six was treated with Zoloft which was escalated to a dose of 125 mg a day over a period of six weeks.

As it turned out the Zoloft didn't work very well. There was a pattern of initial sedation and calming followed by return of symptoms with even worse agitation leading to dosage increases. Harold had difficulty sleeping and experienced nightmares and agitation. He complained of tummy aches and headaches and had diarrhea. The pediatrician knew that things were not working as planned. He recommended a psychiatric consultation. Restrictions from the HMO directed him to someone the pediatrician didn't know and who was new in town. The psychiatrist reviewed the case and decided that Harold needed a more sedating medication and recommended Serzone. He told mom to stop Harold's Zoloft one day and begin some Serzone the next. The next night Harold did sleep a bit. The following day he was incredibly anxious and agitated and crying and this escalated into his running around wildly and screaming and hitting himself and hitting things and attempting to jump out of his bedroom window on the second floor of his home. Harold was hospitalized in a pediatric psychiatric ward.

CHAPTER TEN
HISTORICAL NOTES AND ANECDOTES

When medicine has not found an adequate explanation, or more to the point, an adequate *scientific* explanation, with good hard biochemical and physiologic and cellular data for a troublesome problem that does not respond well to typical treatments, it is frequently called <u>FUNCTIONAL</u>. As in functional psychosis, otherwise known as schizophrenia, a tragic and obviously biological illness. Or as in functional bowel disease. The implication of course is that it's all in the head, and the implication of that is that it's all neurotic, or emotional, or psychological, or in some way reflects a weakness in character or backbone or maturity. No it doesn't quite imply that one is faking it, but one ought really to get a grip. Functional is supposed to be a polite way to say that it's <u>PSYCHOPHYSIOLOGIC</u> OR <u>PSYCHOSOMATIC</u>, two words that push the limits of political rectitude beyond the pale. Shop talk allows that so and so tends to *SOMATACIZE* or to *SOMATIZE* – there is disagreement amongst the cognoscenti as to which slur is more, shall we say, recherché – but that there is "significant supratentorial overlay" goes without saying.

Psychosomatic, negative connotations notwithstanding, refers simply to the mind; psyche and to the body; soma. Psychophysiologic breaks down the same way. The idea is that something in the mind/psyche, a stress, conflict, neurosis, whatever, induces some pathologic effect upon the body/soma. We'll go into this in greater depth later but it is important to realize at this point is the actual difference between mind and brain, the topic long of interest to philosophers, theologians, and some physicians.

In early thoughts about this book, having already developed the main thesis and the review of symptoms noted above, I recalled from my distant past as a resident in psychiatry references to a book about psychosomatic medicine written by the analyst Franz Alexander, MD. I had never seen it but curious tracked it down on the internet. Not surprisingly the title turned out to be PSYCHOSOMATIC MEDICINE, published in 1950. Somewhat surprisingly the diseases listed in the table of contents include: Disturbances of Appetite, Eating, Swallowing, Digestive and Eliminative Functions; Disturbances of Heart Action, Essential Hypertension, Psychogenic Headaches and Migraine; Fatigue State; The Accident Prone Individual; etc.!

There are fascinating references to the hypothalamus and the pituitary and adrenals and the autonomic nervous system. And equally fascinating psychoanalytic explanations for the occurrence of various somatic diseases as a result of intrapsychic conflicts. Anal retentives will delight in the details.

For eons patients have asked, usually with fear and trepidation, the age old question, "what's wrong with me Doc?". And for ages physicians have tried to answer honestly, accurately and gently. Often the response has been a variation on the theme, "I'm not sure," which at least usually is honest. From Hippocrates on the idea of "first, do no harm," has been a truism. Hence, what one tells the patient needs to be as accurate and precise as possible. The reality of an illness is painful enough. The naming of it, the label given, often connotes far more than it denotes, and that may be irrational and frightening.

Diagnostic nomenclature, the formal names of diseases, are codified and re-codified over time. New information leads to the refinement, redesignation, clarification or elimination of prior terms and concepts. Efforts are made to establish international uniformity. Makes sense for the most part. However some efforts may be overreaching in an attempt to sweep away previous concepts in favor of a new order, or to lump together entities that may be symptomatically similar but in fact biologically dissimilar.

No where is this more apparent than in the evolution of the formal psychiatric diagnostic nomenclature in this country since the advent of the D.S.M. III (Diagnostic and Statistical Manual III), first published in 1980 through the iteration of D.S.M. IIIR, 1987, and the current tome D.S.M. IV, 1994, and DSM-IV-TR, 2001.

While there are and have been many criticisms of this manual and the transparently political and social biases present in it , it is a travesty insofar as it clumps together things that really don't belong on the same page, let alone the same chapter (mood disorders, anxiety disorders and eating disorders are examples of this); it minimizes substantial bodies of diagnoses (sleep disorders), and completely ignores others as it creates a new group of mutant concepts to confound reality (neuroses no longer exist but PTSD ((post traumatic stress disorder)) disables the populace). From time to time an article is published which challenges the status quo, asserts the existence of an entity not listed, but the powers that be are obdurate.

In the recent past a variety of useful concepts and specific diagnoses have been legislated into extinction. Doomed with the neuroses were such standbys as involutional melancholia, phobic anxiety syndrome, and atypical hysteroid psychosis to name a few. Where did they go? What happens if your disease is reclassified or abandoned? What if you are still sick? Can you still be treated? But for what? How?

Does it make any sense for you to know that what you have used to be called, say, phobic anxiety, and was known to be exquisitely responsive to a group of medications called Monoamine Oxidase Inhibitors (MAOIs), but that it is now called either a Mood Disorder NOS (not otherwise specified), or an Atypical Mood

Disorder, or maybe a Panic Disorder, or maybe an Anxiety Disorder
NOS, all of which by implication are first treated with SSRI's and
you should get better with them or you are not trying hard enough.

Why is any of this relevant here? Because the nosology is a
ponderous mess. And it leads to sloppy diagnoses. Sloppy
diagnoses and sloppy treatment. It's scary enough to get a
diagnosis. It ought to be precise. It ought to lead to a specific and
correct treatment. Otherwise everything becomes Dermatology 101;
you have a rash, rub some salve on it. It would be simple, at least
for the eye doctor, if everyone were diagnosed with a vision problem
NOS and received the same pair of spectacles. Would you be
comfortable with the diagnosis of, for example, Cancer NOS, and the
simple minded notion that all cancer patients are begun on the same
medication? I think not.

CO-MORBIDITY

Co-morbidity simply means the coincident occurrence of
two or more morbid processes, (morbid in the patois refers to
illness). It does not mean or imply that there is any relationship
between the morbids, just that they are present and active at the
same time. Often co-morbid processes are related: high blood
pressure and heart disease; emphysema and pneumonia; constipation
and hemorrhoids are examples.

As Neuropsychiatric diagnosis with the contributory
confusion offered by the DSM's has gone through its
concatenations, stranger revelations and odd ball ideas are expressed.
For example as early as the early 1980's esteemed authorities in
child psychiatry still insisted that autism was a purely psychological
illness. The same group asserted that children and adolescents did
not and could not have mood disorders, the biological type that is,
major depression and bipolar disorder, and allowed that if in fact an

odd child here or there did have such a problem, one wouldn't treat them with drugs, would one?! Only a proper psychoanalysis would do.

Discussions have rambled for years with various levels of coherence about the relationship of co-morbid depression and anxiety. These tend rapidly to devolve from a gobbledegook of neo-analytic non-sequitors about prenatal fantasy life as it relates to superego lacunae into a miasma of dendritic projections and synaptic receptor electron microscopic architecture as it relates to hemispheric laterality and the limbic system.

Recent journal articles have expounded upon the "discovery" of co-morbid ADHD and bipolar disorder and the need for separate treatment for each, and the existence of co-morbid depression and panic disorder. Stand still for a moment, take a deep breath, let it out slowly, gaze thoughtfully at the list earlier in the book and wonder. Co-morbid? As the kids say; no duh!

The formulation of diagnostic concepts and the comprehension of them is critical in the determination of appropriate treatment. One must understand both a diagnosis and how it is achieved in order to determine proper care. It is the failure to know one or both of these elements that has led to any enormous amount of mismanagement and distress.

Previously I indicated that diagnoses are changed and modified over time. Sometimes this is good, sometimes it is not. We must look further at the DSM to understand the implications of this.

Until DSM III there was a concept of neurosis and neuroses in the diagnostic nomenclature. Indeed this harkened back to Sigmund Freud and psychoanalysis. Simply put a neurosis is a repressed conflict which troubles an individual. Some event or trauma or series of traumas has occurred in the life of a patient, often in an infancy or childhood but also in adolescence or adult life that has caused psychic injury or emotional distress. Unable to deal with this consciously the individual has unconsciously repressed these events and is not able to get in touch with them. These unconscious conflicts smolder along and from time to time in given situations or with certain triggers or provocations emerge to cause emotional and/or physical and/or interpersonal problems for the individual.

Nowadays the concept of neurosis is expressed as Post Traumatic Stress Disorder – PTSD. This has been mentioned before and will be discussed in greater detail later on. But what of neurosis?

After World Was II and into the 1970's American Psychiatry was dominated by psychoanalysis. Not just Freudian psychoanalysis but neo-Freudian, Jungian, Adlerian, Kleinian, Eriksonian, and others. Without devolving into a detailed discussion of these many theoretical approaches the main construct common to all is that an individual's problems have a psychological or emotional root cause. Thus depression, anxiety, psychosomatic afflictions, what have you all have some emotional core that can be understood by a careful unearthing of past memories and experiences and resolution of conflicts that are the source of the distress. If you care to read Alexander's Psychosomatic Medicine you can see how analytic concepts are applied to the various illnesses he discusses.

Through the 70's and into the 80's there was a backlash against analytic psychiatry. Biological psychiatry came to the forefront of psychiatric medicine. The diagnostic nomenclature was restructured.

In DSM III a crosswalk was developed to indicate how various neuroses had been renamed. Thus depressive neurosis became dysthymia and hysterical neurosis became conversion disorder and anxiety neurosis became generalized anxiety disorder.

Then in DSM IIIR and into DSM IV the entire concept and

71

the term neurosis disappeared. With this disappearance was also lost a great deal of knowledge and experience.

For example dysthymia was originally intended to be a non biological form of depression, an emotional or psychological depression coequal to a depressive neurosis. But the concept through the 90's has evolved to see dysthymia as biological, a milder form of major depression. What this has come to mean is that very little if anything remains in modern psychiatry that has to do with emotional or psychological sources. Since everything is directly or by inference biological, it should be amenable to a biological explanation and a biological treatment or therapy. Many of the symptoms may be experienced or expressed in psychological or emotional ways but they are all seen to be biological.

CHAPTER ELEVEN
NEUROSOMATIC CASE REVIEW

Up to now we have given an array of case examples. These have encompassed directly or indirectly all of the complaints on the problem list identified above in the first chapters. Indeed all of the examples have more than one symptom. That is a major element of what we will begin to understand.

Certainly there are people who have only one complaint. There are people who have migraine headaches and none of the other complaints noted on the problem list. There are people who have had an ulcer or colitis without any of the other complaints. Many others have had high blood pressure without these related symptoms. I submit that few people have had Attention Deficit Hyperactivity Disorder or the bulimia described above without having as well other symptoms noted on our problem list. Depression and anxiety are very broad categories and people may have had a depression or anxiety problem without any of the other symptoms. Yet a surprising number have more than one of these complaints throughout their lives.

INTO THE LOOKING GLASS

Now that we have identified this newfangled thing called Neurosomatic, the startling concept that a group of apparently unrelated and supposedly psychosomatic illnesses are in fact all manifestations of a singular brain/body problem, a single illness that can manifest in a protean fashion, it is time to reevaluate our patients within this context. With each one we will crosscheck against our master chart on page 15, see how the multiplicity of symptoms relate, look for the presence of common and consistent physiologic variables and maybe prescribe a different treatment regimen for them. It may not be a single drug regimen. It may require two or three. But in each case we will be treating the central problem not the symptoms, and in some cases appear to be ignoring some of the symptoms completely as we endeavor to solve the problem. As we begin our examination of these patients from a Neurosomatic perspective we will have appropriate and necessary discussions of the key symptoms.

After we have reviewed our patients and helped relieve them of their suffering there will be a necessary discussion of the SSRI's (serotonin selective re-uptake inhibitors) a group of medications widely prescribed in our society which induce, exacerbate, and mask many elements of the Neurosomatic Syndrome to the great distress of millions of patients.

Let us return for a moment to our review of symptoms on page 7. We will tally the score for each of our patients and proceed accordingly.

* * * * * *

Leonard	15
Robert	20
Inez	17
Allan	12
Betty	14
Tiffany	18
Bert	13
Gina	11
Wallace	16
Jerome	12
Mary	16
Frank	10
Lazlo	11
Whitney	10
Maureen	13
Craig	9
Rachael	3

These are the Neurosomatic scores for each of our patients. Yes indeed they are arbitrary. It is difficult to convey in a written description the given intensity and severity of symptoms as described by each and every patient. Suffice to say that the scores are accurate and they support the coexistence – not co-morbidity – of these problems.

IT **IS** ALL IN YOUR HEAD:
A Monograph on Wellness for the New Millennium .

On page 78 is a diagram. It lists vertically the various symptoms of the Neurosomatic Syndrome. The top list of symptoms 1-10 illustrate typical and common treatments of those symptoms. As one can see a patient with two or three or four or more of these symptoms will end up on a veritable smorgasbord of medication. And given the side effects induced by many of these medications, side effects that are sometimes indistinguishable from exacerbation of primary Neurosomatic symptoms, this will lead to more medication for the symptoms and more medication for the side effects.

The bottom, a-b, illustrates correct and effective treatment for the Neurosomatic Syndrome. The primary thrust of treatment is to use noradrenergic antidepressants with GABA ergic medications.

As noted before the biogenic amines involved in mood, anxiety, and various other aspects of psychiatry and neuropsychiatry are noradrenalin, serotonin, and dopamine. If one looks at the typical treatments of Neurosomatic symptoms as illustrated in the left hand column one will see a large number of serotonergic medications. Rarely is a noradrenergic medication contemplated. From time to time a GABA ergic medication will be used but the efficacy of GABA ergic drugs in the face of potent SSRI's is equivocal to nil.

Just to refresh your memory gamma-aminobuteric acid (GABA) is the brain's primary inhibitory neurotransmitter. It is potentiated by a multiplicity of drugs including benzodiazepines (Valium and Xanax group of drugs), and several anticonvulsant medications which include older medicines such as Depakote and Lamictil and newer medicines such as Neurontin, Topamax, and Gabitril.

You may wish to place a bookmark or tag on this chart. As we proceed through the discussion our patients we will reflect upon their prior symptomatic treatment and their present Neurosomatic treatment. You may well wish to compare your own probably very symptomatic care to those of the patients in this book.

<u>WARNING</u>: If you are a patient receiving any form of treatment that may include symptoms, problems, and medications discussed in this book <u>do not</u> repeat <u>do not</u> attempt to alter your care independently or to stop your treatment abruptly. Any change in your care and treatment should be done under the close supervision of an expert physician, neuropsychopharmacologist who understands the concepts elucidated in this book and can help you deal with the profound risks of sudden alterations in your treatment. Of great concern are withdrawal syndromes from such medications as the SSRI's and possibly from benzodiazepines.

IT **IS** ALL IN YOUR HEAD:
A Monograph on Wellness for the New Millennium

THE LONG AND THE SHORT OF IT

1} **A.D.H.D.:** Adderall, Ritalin, Provigil, Wellbutrin, Norpramin...

2} **P.L.M.D.:** Neurontin, Gabitril, Klonopin, Sinemet, Requip...

3} **PANIC/ANXIETY/DEPRESSION:** SSRIs, + something for in sonia, impotence/anorgasmia, GI distress, etc...

4} **BIPOLAR/CYCLOTHYMIA:** Depakote, Lithium, Lamictal, Zyprexa, etc...

5} **H.A./MIGRAINE:** Too numerous to list

6} **I.B.S.:** Antispasmodic, Fiber, SSRI, Sedative

7} **P.U.D.:** H2-blocker, Proton pump inhibitor, antacid, sedative...

8} **G.E.R.D.:** As for P.U.D.

9} **HYPERTENSION:** Too numerous to list

10} **FIBROMYALGIA:** Too numerous to list

OR

NEUROSOMATIC SYNDROME:
a] NORADRENERGIC: Wellbutrin, Adderall, Provigil, Norpramin...

b] GABA-ERGIC: Neurontin, Gabitril, Klonopin...

CHAPTER TWELVE .
THE BLACK HOLE

The morbid depths of depression have been experienced by far too many throughout history for it to continue to be reduced to a character flaw, or lack of backbone in such a callow manner by those who misunderstand it or more to the point fear it. A disease of prodigious prevalence it crosses borders and boundaries in a nondiscriminatory fashion. With a reported incidence greater in women than men, and a frequency that rises with each decade of life, age and gender offer no protection or security. Those afflicted have significant medical co-morbidity. In English that means a greater occurrence of a wide variety of medical problems which often are more difficult to treat. Data on a possible weakened immune system in depression is uncertain. But data on overall frequency and severity of a multitude of ailments as well as diminished compliance with care are clear.

For example, we have alluded to the increased occurrence of high blood pressure in depression. This has a snowball effect. The high blood pressure leads to an increase in stroke, heart attack and arteriosclerosis, which leads to an increase of many more problems and complications.

Depression has a panoply of symptoms. None of them are visible on an x-ray, a brain scan or a blood test. Yes, there are experimental P.E.T. scans (*it means positron emission tomography and has nothing to do with small domestic animals; these are very expensive, of limited availability, not covered by insurance, and redundant when the diagnosis is readily made on clinical examination*), which may suggest certain images consistent with mood disorders. And so, for, generations, because the complaints of the sufferer can't be corroborated by a reproducible scientific test or physical manifestation (for example, a bone bent where there isn't a joint, thus suggesting a fracture!), the complaints have been dubbed emotional, psychological, spiritual, and nervous or functional. Implicit is a weakness in character. Often it's considered downright malingering. Almost always is it an imposition; not on the patient, but upon everyone else.

Despite the absence of a real scientific test (by the by, anyone who says that they can check your serotonin level with a blood test is a fraud) people manifest and suffer a painful litany of reproducible biological changes. Changes in sleep, appetite, energy, interest, motivation, libido, concentration, memory, affect, mood, pleasure, bowel function, perceptual processes, thoughts and thinking abound. Curiously these problems have been catalogued throughout all of recorded human history with greater constancy of experience and a more consistent attribution to source than most any other. Notwithstanding coloured bile's, depression and melancholia were described long before microbes, myocardial infarctions, or Muchausen's syndrome.

Depression with its protean manifestations remains a most common presenting or co-morbid complaint at the doctor's office. Unidentified, untreated or maltreated depression remains the driver behind enormous service utilization, enormous cost and enormous suffering. Yet it remains an uncovered or undercovered health benefit. A victim of depression often becomes a victim of treatment. As they accumulate consultants, procedures and prescriptions for several complaints they can't get a referral to a competent psychiatrist. When the possibility of a **mood disorder** raises its nasty head the patient receives serial SSRI's as per algorithm, or a cocktail of antiquated but cheap, very cheap medicaments that are just as bad if not worse.

What is this thing called depression? It is a biological illness as is diabetes mellitus, gout, or emphysema. Colloquially it is a chemical imbalance. Our present level of sophistication allows us to say that it involves chemicals in the brain called neurotransmitters. Many are involved. Probably all are interrelated at some level beyond our present comprehension. Obviously serotonin is the problem in some cases. But in many the problem is with noradrenalin (noradrenalin is the first cousin of adrenaline, the circulating chemical in the body; it, adrenaline does not cross into the brain across something called the blood-brain barrier, hence the brain produces its own variety). Without doubt but with little data other neurotransmitters are involved. These include acetylcholine, dopamine, gamma-aminobutyric acid (GABA), monoamine oxidase and who knows what else. Certainly some thermostat or servomechanism is out of whack. For sure there is a problem in the hypothalamic pituitary adrenal axis. And certainly input is received from cortical, sub cortical, basal ganglia and brain stem centers, not to mention the body as a whole. Fancy drawings of pathways with neat little arrows and receptors marked D2 and 5 HT and the like are more fanciful than real, typically based upon analysis of nuclear tagged chemicals in homogenized rat brain. Data obtained in the blood, urine or even cerebrospinal fluid of a person is a diluted soup of chemicals and precise attribution to any source is far less accurate than the use of a Ouija board.

Since the prima facie evidence is scarce, what circumstantial data is there? Let's make a list.

1.   Endorphins, the brain's primary feel good substances, released by exercise, narcotics or antidepressants induce a sense of well-being, good feelings, a high.

2.   Cocaine and other stimulants release dopamine and noradrenalin and make some people feel terrific really fast. Some people. Others feel lousy, or sleepy, or nothing at all.

3.   Epileptics who have generalized convulsive seizures, which cause a massive release of neurotransmitters, feel less depressed after a seizure.

4.   Electroconvulsive therapy – Edison Medicine, or shock treatment – induces a generalized brain seizure, releases neurotransmitters, and alleviates depression. It also appears to reset thermostats in the brain. *For example: a) shock treatment is a highly effective if underutilized therapy for Parkinson's Disease, wherein a loss of dopamine producing neurons leads to an imbalance with acetylcholine producing neurons. The treatment releases dopamine and stabilizes the system indefinitely. b.) a common concomitant of head trauma is SIADH – syndrome of inappropriate anti-diuretic hormone, a substance produced in the pituitary and a syndrome that causes serious metabolic disturbance. Shock treatment corrects this problem by resetting the thermostat, probably in the hypothalamus. In both circumstances homeostasis is reestablished.*

If chemicals and drugs and seizures and shocks alleviate, amongst other things, depression, why? Do they just mask or cover over a psychological problem as so many therapists are wont to say? If you believe that you must also believe that toads cause warts and that the plague resulted from spontaneous generation.

The brain is a soft jelly roll of neurons (nerve cells), literally billions of them in a vast microcosmic universe beyond our appreciation. The interconnections, circuits, redundancy, and complexity make the most powerful super computers in the world as advanced as an amoeba, maybe. This is probably an insult to amoebae everywhere. Sorry fellows.

Neurons communicate one to another across a synapse. The synapse is the gap between the end of one neuron and the beginning of the next. The first transmits the message to the second via the release of chemicals, neurotransmitters, produced in the former, received by the latter, at a site called a receptor. Multiple steps along the way pose potential problems. Consider: inadequate production; insufficient release; receptor insensitivity; too rapid degradation of the transmitter; or, overproduction/overactivity of another system.

Antidepressant medications work in a similar variety of ways. Increased production, increased release, decreased degradation. Or nuke it with electricity and shake everything loose.

Crude though the data may be it is real. What on earth does this have to do with potty training, self-esteem or your inner child. This is a **disease**, an **illness**, as is lupus, or glaucoma or pneumonia.

CHAPTER THIRTEEN
HISTORICAL NOTES AND ANECDOTES
HORSE FEATHERS

There are three biogenic amine neurotransmitters in the brain involved in mood, anxiety, attention, and other Neuropsychiatry functions pertinent to our discussion. All three of these biogenic amine neurotransmitters are degraded or digested by the enzyme monoamine oxidase.

Research into the unfortunate disease schizophrenia has focused extensively on the neurotransmitter dopamine. Along the way a parallel body of research data was developed on the neurotransmitter serotonin. The third biogenic amine neurotransmitter noradrenalin has been ignored for a long time despite excellent data that is the primary transmitter involved in a great number of mood and anxiety disorders.

Some have said that noradrenalin is to be the neurotransmitter of the new millennium. Virtually all antidepressants in development at this time are noradrenergic antidepressants.

To assert that all depression is biological is as accurate as to assert that all quadrupeds are horses. To assert that all biological depressions are mediated by and responsive to serotonin is to believe that horses can fly.

There is a body of literature that has developed since the late 1960's which refers to the difference between noradrenergic and serotonergic depression. A fellow named Maas authored a slew of articles about this. Most importantly he wrote that in the assessment and differential diagnosis of the depressed patient, with a particular view towards treatment strategies, a single dose stimulant trial with 10 mg of Dexedrine might be helpful. A depressed patient who perks up and feels better and brighter and calmer on a single dose of speed should be treated with a noradrenergic agent. A dysphoric response should lead to the prescription to a serotonergic agent. If the response is uninterpretable then the treatment is empirical.

Furthermore it is well known that in cocaine abuse and addiction the neurotransmitters involved are noradrenalin and dopamine. It is also known that treatment of such individuals (who often have undiagnosed mood and attention disorders, cardinal symptoms of a Neurosomatic Syndrome) with noradrenergic agents can improve their moods and diminish cravings and relapse. Pure dopaminergic agents (mobilize dopamine) are useless, so the smart money is on noradrenalin.

Question: Why give these people an SSRI?

Answer: It says so in the cookbook.

The brain is a very complicated organ with an enormous amount happening in a very small space. Do I really believe that this is noradrenalin alone? No. But the gross overemphasis to this point upon serotonin and dopamine, for the combined reasons that there has been a technology to measure them as well as drugs to affect them has led to misinterpretation of data. It is not possible to alter the balance of one biogenic amine without having an impact on the others. This is simple logic that has been ignored. While there are studies that can show supposed damage to serotonergic and dopaminergic neurons in patients who abuse cocaine the interpretation of this data again has been teleological as opposed to rational. A simple reflection on cause and effect of the different drugs available prove the point. It is also apparent that the effects on dopamine and serotonin are downstream of the noradrenalin effects

CHAPTER FOURTEEN
TWENTY WINKS OR NAME YOUR POISON

What would you give for a good night's sleep? When did you last get one? Would you know it if you got one or might it be so peculiar that you would think it was abnormal; you know, restful, unmedicated, just the right amount, wake refreshed?

What difficulties have you with your sleep? Can't seem to fall asleep? Frequent early morning awakening and can't get back to sleep? Can't get up in the morning? Always tired, never get enough rest? Toss and turn and kick your partner and tear up the bed? Have some odd twitches and jerks as you drift off to sleep? Grind your teeth so badly you have TMJ (*temporal mandibular joints syndrome*) and need a bite block and maybe jaw surgery? Get up depressed and grouchy and stiff with sore muscles and ache all over and in particular in the neck and shoulder and with sore joints and may be a headache? Does your mind churn ruminatively, obsessively, over and over about anything and everything?

Try to remember way back when. As a child you slept better, or did you? Were you truly a good sleeper then? Or didn't you notice some early signs because kids aren't supposed to have sleep problems and you seemed to do okay for the most part. Did you kick around and rip the bed apart every night (you might have to ask mom)? Did you not seem to need much sleep and stay up reading in the dark when you weren't supposed to? Did a dentist remark that you ground your teeth and tell you to stop? Were you a bright student who was easily bored by pedantic teaches and tended to drift off into your own much more interesting thoughts and sometimes actually nod off during a particularly banal film strip?

You've got a lot on your mind and you're all wound up and you have so much to do and there doesn't seem to be enough time anymore and if it's not one thing it's another and . . .

IT **IS** ALL IN YOUR HEAD:
A Monograph on Wellness for the New Millennium

One way or another you'll get some sleep. What potion, what balm or unguent will salve your ragged nerves. Name your poison. What'll it be? How about a sleeping pill? What's new? Ambien, Halcion, Melatonin, Trazadone, Sonata. What isn't? Dalmane, Noctec, Placidyl, Doriden, Tuinal, Seconal, Nembutal, Quaalude, Benadryl. Or, of course, booze! The famous two carbon killer, alcohol. To a lesser or greater degree all with knock you out, briefly, sort of, more or less. All are sedatives. None of them induce true, genuine, honest to goodness sleep. Cheap anesthesia is about all you get, with or without a buzz. Quantity, not quality.

Unconsciousness is not sleep. It is, well, being knocked out or doped up to the point of insensate blubbery. It does not, even remotely, meet basic criteria for the functions of sleep.

Probably the most common sleep problems are behavioral insomnia and hypnotic dependence. Frequently missed is the problem of sleep apnea as well as the more subtle forms of narcolepsy. Usually missed and quite problematic is the non-restorative sleep syndrome of alpha delta sleep associated with Restless Legs Syndrome or Periodic Limb Movement Disorder. And of course, that scourge, "fibromyalgia". When you are convinced erroneously that you must have the same sleep every night – fall asleep at the same time, never be disturbed, wake refreshed at the same time, always – you have a problem. Day to day variations in stress, anxiety, fatigue, caffeine, foods, alcohol, medications, viruses and the environment all impact your sleep. While you might not enjoy a bad night's sleep from time to time it isn't a problem unless you make it one. If you grab a drink, a pill or a prescription immediately you will become hypnotic dependent quickly. If you commence to obsess about your sleep, worry whether or not you will fall asleep easily and sleep well, you won't.

But if you let it ride, don't lie in the dark and brood and

worry and flop about waiting for sleep, but instead, get up turn on a light, listen to music, channel surf until you are drowsy and then sleep a bit you will nip the problem in the bud. Attention to the variables mentioned above is a good idea as well. Maybe that evening meeting that upset you or the coffee and cola or the fight with the kid or the nagging cold and decongestants are culprits.

If you don't address behavioral issues and you have an abundance of rationalizations why you can't make any changes in your life then you need an excellent therapist. If you do everything right and you still have a problem then you need an excellent diagnostic evaluation.

If you reach for a pill or a potion - a "sleeper" in the parlance with ease and frequency, often in a very brief period of time you become dependent upon it. Not in the craving out of control dependence of heroin but the absolutely ain't gonna sleep at all without it kind of dependence. And the annoying rebound insomnia that occurs when you stop; you can't sleep at all once the drug stops and it takes at least two weeks to re-equilibrate to the native level of sleep or sleep disturbance, and if you try to cheat and take a sleeper to combat the rebound insomnia you simply continue the hypnotic dependence and defer the rebound. This is a very bad strategy; the effectiveness of virtually all sleepers if used regularly attenuates rapidly leading to endless dose increases or dangerous combinations. In short, other than for very occasional use sleepers are a bad idea.

Sleep apnea often is overlooked. No, you don't <u>have</u> to be morbidly obese with a thick short neck, smoke, take alcohol and sedatives before bed and snore louder than chain saws to have sleep apnea. You may have no apparent risk factors at all other than you snore sometimes usually on your back. You may have florid breath holding, gasp and grunt patterns or you may only have what appear to be slight irregular breathing patterns and momentary breath holding; may be with a little gasp or sigh from time to time. You may still have sleep apnea with depression, high blood pressure, memory problems, irritability and excessive daytime sleepiness. Someone needs to ask you about all of this and be able to put it all together. And yes someone other than you may need to stay up for a while one night and observe your sleep. Be nice.

Narcolepsy is rare. It is a disorder caused by a jumbling of sleep rhythms. You may fall into deep sleep mid sentence, or dream while you are awake, or awaken in deep sleep and feel paralyzed. It is serious. It is not really central to this book but warrants comment anyhow. The five major characteristics of Narcolepsy are: excessive daytime sleepiness, not just falling asleep, you go directly from awake to sleep with no transitional phase; hypnogogic and hypnopompic hallucinations, hallucinations as you fall asleep or wake up are dreams when you aren't supposed to be dreaming and they seem like hallucinations; cataplexy, sudden muscle weakness, even to the point of collapse, sometimes triggered by laughter or yawning as your body but not your brain goes into deep sleep at the wrong time; sleep paralysis, you awaken or believe you are awake but feel totally paralyzed for a while, can't move a muscle, as your brain awakens while your body is still in deep sleep; automatic behaviors, occur as you sleep walk and do things that may seem quite normal to things that seem pretty goofy, such as putting your socks in the fridge or making a phone call with a camera. If you experience any of these talk to a knowledgeable specialist.

Presently we'll take a look at the other sleep problems mentioned. But to do so sensibly we must do just a tad more science.

Let's take twenty winks and review what sleep is and what it does. There is so little grasp of good sleep that we shall have to explicate it briefly as a necessary step to an examination of lousy sleep, the kind that many of us seem to get more often than not.

Sleep is a most necessary phase of our natural daily cycle. Restful, restorative, but poorly understood, it serves a function for both the brain and the body. Without it, we cannot survive, let alone function or feel well. Sleep is a critical part of our diurnal circadian rhythms. It occupies about one third of our life. It must serve a purpose.

Recall if you will those bygone days of yesteryear when you slept like a baby. You were a baby then, ostensibly without a care in the world and your sleep was untroubled. Let's defer the psychologizing and look at the physiology.

Infants eat and sleep, hopefully all through the night if you are a parent. As they grow and do sleep through the night they seem to have two speeds, on or off. They buzz around to exhaustion (yours), then fall asleep. Their naps evolve into a pattern of morning and afternoon and the afternoon nap lingers for quite a while longer than the morning snooze. This pattern is consistent with the lifelong human circadian rhythm.

We all have a down time in the mid to late afternoon. Long before polysomnograms where a twinkle in anyone's eye many cultures identified this cycle and took an afternoon siesta. Americans ignore this pattern. Too bad. Did you ever wonder why there are more traffic accidents in the evening rush hour than in the morning one? Maybe people don't fall asleep at the wheel just because they are tired; maybe they fall asleep because they are supposed to.

Sleep deteriorates, gets worse as we age. Quantity decreases as does quality and efficiency. Enjoy it while you are young. Pundits notwithstanding not everyone needs or gets eight hours of sleep every night. And whatever your baseline quantity is as a young adult it will decrease with age.

This is a serious problem with many elderly patients who are obsessed with the idea that they must have eight hours of sleep. They go to bed at 9:00 PM only to awaken at 1:00 or 1:30 AM, fully refreshed and having had their night's sleep. But it's the middle of the night! So they take a sleeping pill and try to sleep until 6:00 or 7:00 AM. And then when they get up at 4:00 AM to go to the bathroom they are sedated, stumble, trip and fall. Fractured skulls and hips have shortened the lives of many people. Late night television is made for these people. Once they can be educated to maintain a normal sleep/wake cycle, get up early, exercise, take a short nap in the afternoon, say thirty or forty minutes and then stay up until midnight or 1:00 AM, then go to bed and get a good four or five hours of sleep and so forth and so on, they do quite well.

There are different phases of sleep. For purposes of simplicity we will need to understand three of them; alpha or light sleep, delta or deep sleep, and R.E.M. (rapid eye movement) or paradoxical sleep.

Alpha is a light sleep you experience when you doze, half asleep, half awake, aware of your environment, but not interactive with it, unfocused mentally, <u>drifting off</u> to sleep. Alpha is relaxing. It is not restful. Alpha is the state autogenic gurus and biofeedback merchants try to help you achieve. In alpha your brain is still awake, albeit tuned down (zoned out used to describe it well) and you continue to have tension in your muscles. Alpha is the phase unfortunate narcoleptics skip when they nod off.

R.E.M. is dream sleep. It is called rapid eye movement sleep because it was apprehended that vigorous, rapid but random eye movements occur during this phase. It is called paradoxical because if it weren't for the fact that you were asleep it would seem you were *awake. The brain is furiously busy; your muscle tone is increased and there is some muscle movement; there is significant arousal with increased pulse and engorgement of erectile tissues. Much is madeof the content of dreams by some psychoanalysts. This is interesting and now and then useful. But for our purposes think of dream activity as the brain's necessary conclusion to the day. It sorts and reviews and classifies and <u>uploads</u> data from its RAM to its hard disk. Immediate memory can last up to twenty hours; it is an electrochemical memory. When the brain makes a permanent memory it actually makes some new nucleic acids that get put somewhere. By extension this intense brain activity triggers or drives a multitude of body systems (nervous energy may be a double entendre), as it quite literally unwinds from the days work.*

Delta is the deepest sleep, dreamless, when your muscles are completely flaccid. Have you ever picked up a sleeping child? Sometimes they have muscle tone and nuzzle up to you – alpha. At other times they seem to grumble and fuss and resist a bit, as if you were interfering with something – R.E.M. And then there are the times when they are as limp as a wet noodle, floppy and cumbersome and you have to take great care to lie them down because they make no effort to help – delta. Delta is the most necessary part of sleep. It is the most restorative. R.E.M. deprivation can make you irritable and nasty. Delta deprivation can make you totally irrational. It appears that delta offers both the brain and the body a period of complete relaxation, rest and restoration. Pulse, respiration and breathing idle down and the cortex muscles and just about everything else rests, heals, recovers, and gets ready to get up the next day.

Previously we mentioned alpha-delta sleep. This is a core problem that will be elaborated upon in greater depth later. For the present it is important to understand the fundamental aspects of it. Ponder this for a while. If alpha sleep intrudes continuously into delta sleep, what happens? Given what we know so far we might posit that regular sleep cycles are disturbed, that the brain never gets to turn off and rest completely, that the body and its muscles never stop and relax and become at ease and achieve a complete natural cycle. More to come.

CHAPTER FIFTEEN
SEE HARDER, BREATHE EASIER

Oh yeh, A.D.D. again, or A.D.H.D.   You mean those hyperactive kids, the mouthy ones who just don't pay attention and are disruptive troublemakers. They are just behavior problems with bad attitudes, right? And you just dope them up with Ritalin and after a while they grow out of it and become difficult troubled adolescents. They don't really need treatment or medications or therapy or accommodations or understanding. They just need to brace up, get with the program.

Now this a nice, nincompoop's approach to a biological medical problem. Quite sensible, don't you think. About as smart as to deny a severely myopic child glasses and to insist that she just **see harder**. Or to take away an asthmatics inhaler and to demand that he **breathe easier**.

This has nothing to do with food coloring, bleached flour or allergies. It does have something to do with sugar, but not what most people think. This is a biologically based problem, is strongly heritable, and too often misdiagnosed and mismanaged. This is more a difference of attention issue than a deficit of attention. It does seem that there a large group of folks whose cerebral operations are a bit different than the average or mean group. What are some of the characteristics?

1.   Left handedness or mixed dominance (it's hard to say if this is true mixed or confused dominance or if a lot of natural south paws got switched as babies).
2.   High intelligence.
3.   Creativity, often artistic.
4.   Attention/focus, trouble maintaining it, particularly if disinterested.

5.   Easily distracted.
6.   Easily bored, easily frustrated.
7.   Daydreamer; one's own thoughts much more interesting than teachers or managers.
8.   Procrastination.
9.   Difficulty getting organized, difficulty getting started.
10.   Lots of projects and thoughts going on at once; starts a lot of projects but trouble finishing them.
11.   Impatient.
12.   Impulsive.
13.   Risk taking.
14.   Clumsiness/ accident prone.
15.   Moody.
16.   Worrier, looks for things to worry about.
17.   Anxiety.
18.   Rejection sensitive.
19.   Low self-esteem.
20.   Difficulty going through regular (bureaucratic) channels.
21.   Lack of awareness or misperception of social situations.
22.   Seeks stimulation.
23.   Tremendous capacity for nonlinear reasoning.
24.   Sleep problems; poor sleepers; stay up very late sleepers; don't sleep much sleepers;*almost all with non-restorative alpha delta sleep whether or not they manifest restless legs or myoclonus.*
25.   Develop many compensatory strategies unconsciously. Often misdiagnosed with Obsessive Compulsive Disorder (O.C.D.). Often quite "Type A".
26.   The sugar thing. See Chapter eighteen.
27.   Difficulty handling transitions.

IT **IS** ALL IN YOUR HEAD:
A Monograph on Wellness for the New Millennium

Gee whiz, say you. That's a pretty encompassing list. Might fit a lot of people. It does, say I. The numbers of undiagnosed, misdiagnosed and mismanaged cases are legion. In the next chapters we will begin to assemble the pieces of our puzzle and all of this will come together.

Hyperactive kids are hard to miss. The restless, fidgety, tapping, yapping, squirming, poking, get up and hop around the room, ignore the teacher and hoot, won't go to bed and the room would look neater if hit by a tornado, and can't seem to pay attention to anything for more than thirty seconds except of course Nintendo and then you can't distract them with a bugle, hyperactive sort of kid might get noticed. No sweat.

But what about all of the other kids, and the adults who once were kids, the ones who were quietly bored, easily distracted. Daydreamers, who were told that they were smart but lazy, not working up to their potential, indifferent, had a bad attitude and were smart alecks. The ones whose school performance always seemed to start great and then tail off by midyear. The ones who showed so much promise in grade school but who had progressive difficulty in middle school or high school as the structure decreased and the need for individual organizational abilities increased. The ones who always pulled it together at the last minute to complete the term paper or project. The ones who never seemed able or willing to sit through interminable discussions or meetings and couldn't tolerate cretinous bureaucratic nonsense and said so and <u>always</u> seem to be like the <u>fool</u> in the emperor's new clothes and always pointedly told the principal that fat old ladies like her shouldn't demonstrate how she used to jitterbug and told the boss his new toupee looked like it needed to be fed.

Along the way the more successful ones developed compensatory strategies to deal effectively with school and work and life. Often they were misdiagnosed as having O.C.D. because they used obsessive mechanisms to succeed; always put things in the same place so they could find them later; start a new project immediately and storm through it until done (before one lose interest or got distracted) and blew your top if someone interrupted you. Then they were treated with, guess what? SSRI's. Guess what else? They didn't work.

CHAPTER SIXTEEN
A BUNDLE OF NERVES

"Calm down, why don't you . . . what's the big deal . . . don't get so worked up . . . chill out, cool your jets . . . what are you so worried about . . . you're just a bundle of nerves!"   Have you ever heard, or said one of these soothing, comforting, empathic nostrums as someone's massive anxiety is about to blossom into a full-blown, hyperventilated, pain in the chest, everything is closing in fast – very fast – panic attack? Terrific reassurance, calms them right down, no? No.

Anxiety, and depression, are incomprehensible to one who has not experienced them. When one does they are indescribable, the words used can't genuinely convey the palpable misery experienced. Which says nothing for the comfort given by such sensitive encouragement as that above.

Anxiety is not by definition abnormal. Nor is it always unpleasant. Anxiety is a signal that we give ourselves. It alerts us, heightens awareness, vigilance. Recall if you will the fight/flight effect of the sympathetic nervous system. When we nervously await our blind date and fidget and pace and check our hair or tie or make-up for the nineteenth time we are anxious. When we eagerly anticipate the kickoff at the Super Bowl and fidget and pace and chatter we are anxious. The former is given a negative valence, the latter a positive one. You know that you are anxious, but you also know why. When we feel anxious for no particular reason, don't know why, we start to worry about why we're worried, or worry that we will worry, and we worry some more in an endless downward spiral of anxiety, apprehension, frustration, and sometimes panic.

Precisely how distinct Panic Disorder is from general anxiety is unclear. There are many ways to examine it. But for our purposes we must look at what anxiety is, what it does, and what to do about it, with some thought about whence it comes.

Recall the description of sympathetic nervous system arousal: increased pulse (rapid heart beat, the palpitations of anxiety); increased respiration's (rapid breathing; blows off carbon dioxide and causes light headedness, numbness and tingling about the face and the extremities, visual changes, almost a swoon – certainly the sudden and rapid consumption of blood sugar only worsens the sensations); increased muscle tone (that tightening in your chest, neck, shoulders, jaw); increased vigilance (but of what; if there is nothing real to fear out there you are just that much more aware of your distress which only makes it worse); restlessness (you feel the need to move, anywhere, although some are so frightened that they are virtually paralyzed and can't even try to escape from themselves). This dreadful experience drives itself, takes on its own existence, and can be disabling. And not to forget, this sympathetic arousal abruptly zaps the parasympathetic nervous system. Your stomach and bowels freeze, and eventually you begin to add all those delightful symptoms of a "nervous bowel".

The notion that some anxiety is normal is anathema to many people, to too many therapists and to too many physicians. I said physicians in general because it is meaningful to know that most psychotropic drugs are not prescribed by psychiatrists. Most are doled out by family physicians, gynecologists, internists, gerontologists, cardiologists, you name it, and a large number of nurse practitioners, none of whom have any expertise in psychiatric diagnosis, psychiatric treatment, or psychopharmacology. Many follow treatment algorithms (cookbooks) provided by insurance companies. Most take umbrage at the notion that they shouldn't fiddle with this stuff. But watch how nuts they go if a psychiatrist has the audacity to adjust a patient's blood pressure or bowel regimen!

Efforts to treat anxiety are as old as recorded history; probably older. When the first batch of fruits or grains or gruel went sour, fermented into a sour mash alcohol containing anxiolytic glop, the treatment began. Brewing and fermentation are common to most cultures throughout history. And for those unfamiliar with the process the use of innumerable roots and weeds served a similar purpose. Hemp, valerian, coca, peyote, opium, thebaine to name a few. Plus healing salts and mineral waters usually with lithium or bromine as the active but unknown ingredient. A bromide was a calmative often combined with an alkaline salt to ease the digestion. To take a powder was to take a sedative. Of course too much of a one led to toxicity or poisoning. The once popular Mickey Finn is a mixture of chloral hydrate powder in alcohol. When one was slipped a "Mickey" one did not wake up.

Thus it has been throughout history. Man has sought constantly for relief from stress and anxiety. Yes, all of the substances mentioned have been misused and abused and some folks have sought to escape any real feelings in a chemical fog. Nonetheless anxiety and attempts to treat it are not new.

This century the primary categories of anxiolytics besides alcohol have been opiates (i.e. tincture of), barbiturates (i.e. butisol), carbamates (i.e. Miltown) and benzodiazepines (i.e. valium). The gamut of antidepressants have been tried culminating in the obsessive national delusion with the Selective Serotonin Reuptake Inhibitors, the notorious SSRI's (i.e. Paxil and Prozac).

A perpetual confounding variable in all attempts to treat anxiety, regardless of how prudent, appropriate and effective those attempts be, is the puritanical view that anything that makes you feel good is inherently bad and evil. This has been clothed in many secular and philosophical arguments, ordinarily hawking the faith, therapy or ideology of the critic, universally assailing the prescription, the prescriber and the prescribee.

It can be difficult and obviously subjective to decide how much of one's anxiety is normal, particularly when it isn't yours. It is important. As we proceed through this book I will try to frame and reframe these concepts carefully.

Others have discussed anxiety as being state dependent, a function of circumstance or situation, while others state that anxiety is a trait, with some folks being naturally more anxious than others. Both are correct in the general sense. Most folks might agree that one or another situation provokes anxiety, oh, maybe like becoming a parent. Most folks might also agree that some folks are just a tad more nervous than the rest. Why?

For ages it has been stated and implied that the anxious person is emotionally flawed. It's in the psyche not the soma. A problem or a weakness or a neurosis or a hang-up is the origin of the problem and drives the somatic reactions which occur. Psyche to soma, the mind drives the body and it becomes a vicious cycle thereafter. Where it began ceases to be of any immediate interest to the sufferer. This notion pays the mortgage for herds of therapists devoted to the discovery of your repressed memories whether you have any or not.

In fact neurotic anxiety does occur. But not always. Could there be an alternate explanation to the mind/body, psyche/soma theorem that dominates treatment and labels patients?

Previously we described the need for homeostasis in <u>all</u> of the body's systems. We have also established that the anxious person seems stuck in a hypersympathetic state – too much adrenaline. Clearly the experience of this condition is anxiety. Let's add a few more pieces of information.

First, notwithstanding fatuous assertions about the intrapsychic life of infants and small children, it is abundantly obvious that some newborns are anxious and that they become anxious toddlers, anxious children and anxious adults. They may have wonderful parents and calmer siblings but they, for no good reason, are anxious. And throughout their lives they experience much of what we've described thus far.

Second, when with modest treatment anxiety is controlled, besides the alleviation of many related symptoms the patient ceases to worry (not ceases to care) about all those worrisome things. Might it be that the anxiety is a native if abnormal physiological state and that the busy mind needs to find something about which to worry? The brain, the body of the nervous system, the ultimate driver and home of all of those thermostats, victim of a chemical/neurotransmitter imbalance worries. The bowels cramp, the stomach burns, and the brain anxiously worries.

We will go into to this more as we proceed, but for now ponder the thought that all of that anxiety, all of that worry has no primary emotional source, no primary intrapsychic meaning. Maybe it's just the way the brain experiences and the mind interprets this "nervous energy". Maybe there is not anything such as psychosomatic or psychophysiologic after all. Maybe it's Neurosomatic, a brain/body thing.

CHAPTER SEVENTEEN
YOU CAN'T EAT AND RUN

Imagine the scene, the Boston Marathon. World class runners from every corner of the globe pound the pavement towards Heartbreak Hill. Along the route, where once the runners grabbed a quick sip of water, or some Gatorade, now stand commercial outlets, corporate sponsored, hawking their goods. Will the graceful Kenyan grab a Big Mac or a Whopper. Will ethnic preferences prevail? Will the Mexican runner glide by the Taco Bell? Will the Japanese competitor sidle up to the sushi bar? Will there be ponies of draught beer in keen plastic cups? And, the single most important question, which French fries will the leaders grab?

Disgusted yet? Can't stomach jogging down Main Street, a double chili cheeseburger in one hand, a burrito in the other? Why not? Think it might sit there in you stomach like a brick, not be digested comfortably and forthwith? Right! So, why do you treat your alimentary canal so foolishly?

If we begin at the top we suffer reflux esophagitis, now renamed gastroesophageal reflux disease, heartburn, dyspepsia, indigestion, gastric ulcers, gastritis, peptic ulcers, irritable bowel syndrome and diverticulitis. Each one listed has a variety of other names as well. Physicians have a broad selection of nifty and fun tests to examine these problems, from the top, bottom, or anywhere in between.

And what might the symptoms be? Oh, there is that burning right under the breastbone that creeps up through your chest to the back of your throat, often accompanied by that acid taste in your mouth. Or that heavy sensation, too full, right after you eat, that weighs you down like gravel ballast, and your stomach knots up around it and you aren't sure what direction it will go but you really want it to go anywhere as long as it goes away. Or the dense, boring fire, about an hour after you eat, not exactly under the sternum, that sometimes isn't so bad when the cramps in your abdomen and nauseous urge distract you.

Sundry appurtenances include gas and burps and those overly loud squishy emanations from your tummy that only happen when the room is very quiet and you're trying to be serious and in control. The gurgles and burbles squeeze their way around and your skirt or your pants have definitely, magically shrunk at least two sizes in less than an hour and all you ate was pasta salad and mineral water.

But those are the little cramps, the counterpoint to the genuine double over and gasp and hold onto whatever very tight cramps that wring and bite and twist about in your colon and you begin to perspire and look earnestly for a toilet because this one might not cease and maybe you won't be able to hold it until . . .

The periods, unpredictable of course, of alternating diarrhea and constipation, regardless of how assiduously you follow the diet (high fiber or low fiber, it depends upon the current consensus). The embarrassment and distress of the gas (except for fraternity boys of all ages). And the dreadful moment when you look forward more to your next bowel movement then your next orgasm.

Remember Health Class. You chew food to break it down and saliva moistens it and begins the digestive process as some carbohydrates are broken down to sugar. What you chewed slides down your esophagus and into your stomach where hydrochloric acid is released and the stomach further mashes up the stuff so that it can be squeezed along with a soup of other digestive juices and enzymes through the pylorus and into the duodenum and ooze its merry way along the small intestine (duodenum to jejunum to ileum; sounds like a Roman infield, doesn't it?) where, aided by legions of bacteria the food is actually digested and the nutrients absorbed, until it reaches the ileo-cecal valve. What passes through there is digestive jetsam. As it slogs around the colon (ascending, horizontal and descending) the moisture is absorbed and resorbed until the stuff twists back through the sigmoid and makes a Bee line for the rectum.

Digestion is a slow, methodical, sedentary process. Generally it takes about 24 hours from ingestion to elimination. Herbivores eat all the time and lumber about slowly, getting out of low gear but rarely, and only to get away from a prospective date or to avoid becoming someone else's snack. Carnivores gorge themselves and then sleep it off. Humans, for the most part, eat and run.

If we remember our basic science, digestion is a parasympathetic function. Regulation and release of the digestive juices, stimulation of the smooth involuntary muscle of the intestines to contract in rhythmic waves of peristalsis, control of the sphincter muscles (the valves at the end of the esophagus, stomach, small intestine and colon), and absorption of nutrients and their transformation into you.

The primary transmitter involved here, parasympathetic that is, is acetylcholine. The system is called cholinergic. We have not mentioned that before but it is very important to know. You will see as we proceed.

As you know, when the parasympathetic nervous system cranks up, the sympathetic nervous system cranks down. Or that's supposed to be the way it works.

Think for a moment about that marathon runner. Chugging along mile after mile his/her body is 100% sympathetic: heart pounds, muscles burn enormous amounts of oxygen and glucose. Glucose, your blood's sugar, comes from your body's reserve of glycogen, and then from the catabolism (metabolic breakdown) of protein. At that point the body can't really burn fat into glucose, and how much fat does the average marathoner have, anyway? As they say; "the old adrenaline is pumping". And when it does, it pretty much shuts down most parasympathetic activity. This includes of course your gut. Thus in an adrenergic state digestive functions freeze. That tasty taquito will sit there in your belly like so much cement. In the adrenergic state the body, and specifically the gut can't digest or absorb much of anything, let alone deep fried delicacies. It can handle water, salts (electrolytes such as those typically found in Gatorade), and invert sugar (honey). These items don't need any digestion, they just go right in. Complex carbohydrates, fats and proteins are as useful to the body in an adrenergic state as is toothpaste to a clam.

Great, you say next time you run a marathon you'll take special care to avoid deep fat for the duration. How does that bear upon everyday life. A lot of folks stumble around the neighborhood in their skivvies and call it a jog, but what does all of this have to do with us regular earthlings?

Reflect for a moment if you will on your life, your lifestyle, the problem list above, and the case examples. Ponder the description of anxiety. Think about what happens when you have a headache. Is something going on? Might there be something adrenergic happening? Yep. For generations digestive disturbances have been treated with anticholinergics. Anticholinergics are also called antispasmodics; they diminish the involuntary muscle spasm experienced as cramps. Unfortunately anticholinergics do little to diminish other digestive functions, hydrochloric acid excretion for example, nor do they dispose of that stuff you ate for the past 48 hours and lies inert in your tum-tum. Oh, and by the way, anticholinergics have no impact on the sympathetic system. It isn't turned down because the parasympathetic is zapped. It zooms along unchallenged.

A panoply of medicaments have evolved to mollify the bowels. Antacids, H2 blockers, acid secretion inhibitors, and stool softeners. None of them effect any reasonable balance with the sympathetic nervous system.

A few older remedies (Donnatal, Librax,) contained a sedative/anxiolytic. These are rarely used by modern croakers who find the use of such substances untenable. And heaven forbid the mention of paregoric (tincture of opium) which diminished bowel spasm and calmed folks.

Confusion arose over the past decade with the discovery of H. Pylori. H. Pylori is a bacterium, first isolated, take a guess, in the pylorus. That's the location of eons of pyloric/duodenal ulcers, the kind that nervous, neurotic, psychosomatic type folks get. Then they found it in gastric ulcers too, the nasty ominous kind that precede stomach cancer. Well, surprise surprise, these ulcers healed when treated with antibiotics that killed the H. Pylori bacterium, supplemented with something to stop the acid secretion for a couple of weeks, that to stop the irritation and to permit healing to occur.

None of this has anything to do with sympathetic activity. Nor is there any data to address the question of whether the blocked parasympathetic/cholinergic system creates an environment that promotes the growth and development of H. Pylori, the culprit in so much of "psychosomatic" gastrointestinal distress.

There are no data at all about the possible infectious causes of the infamous inflammatory bowel diseases Ulcerative Colitis and Crohn's Disease, although antibiotics are a mainstay of treatment for them. There are obvious physiologic and anatomic mechanisms in irritable bowel disease and the development of diverticulosis, hemorrhoids and such like.

Is there a point here? Yep. You betcha. For the time being, keep in mind and begin to ponder about sympathetic and parasympathetic, cholinergic and anticholinergic, and all that boring science stuff.

IT **IS** ALL IN YOUR HEAD:
A Monograph on Wellness for the New Millennium

CHAPTER EIGHTEEN
THE SUGAR BOOGIE

Eating disorders of one sort or another (hang on to that "another") have become so common in our culture that if not the norm in some places they are at least chic. All women are supposed to look like a Cosmo cover girl, or at worst, a run of the mill Parisian runway model. Gaunt, hollow cheeked, long legged, lean, svelte and hungry. Most especially hungry. Or more to the point, downright starved. As in Anorexic. Besides models, gymnasts and ballerinas seem more often than not to have an eating disorder.

There is a very bad disease, a potentially fatal disease, a frequently improperly treated disease called Anorexia Nervosa. It is characterized by a distorted body image, feeling always too fat, calorie restriction, compulsive exercise, laxative, diuretic and emetic abuse, and purging (a fancy name for self-induced vomiting). This disease has some relationship to obsessive compulsive disorder (OCD) and some forms of depression. Pharmacologically it responds well to serotonergic agents, drugs that increase the availability of a neurotransmitter called serotonin at some place in your brain. While this is important, we aren't going to address Anorexia Nervosa here in any depth, but remember that red herring, serotonin, because it will raise it's ugly little head regularly as we proceed. What we want to examine is Anorexia Nervosa's phony cousin Bulimia, queen of the binge.

Bulimia, bulimia nervosa; bularexia, binge eating disorder; compulsive overeating. These terms are bandied about daily, generally interpreted to be about the same thing, and a separate but related entity to Anorexia Nervosa. It is subsumed under the category heading of Eating Disorders in the holy book of diagnoses with dreadful results.

Clearly there are a variety of Bulimia's. Some are sad but simple – gluttony on the one hand and people who just eat too much and don't really want to stop on the other. And there are some pre Anorexic and some post Anorexic patients in whom the illness waffles back and forth from eating too much to eating too little. One must enquire carefully with this population for it is not uncommon for the unfortunate Anorexic to claim the need to purge after a binge when the binge amounted to a total of seven grapes or one half of a small container of fat free yogurt.

There is a very distinctive group with a very distinctive pattern of bulimia or bingeing. This is a large group (no pun intended). Again, close questioning is necessary. Mostly a history of bingeing or gorging is obtained without any relevant detail. Upon <u>what</u> precisely does the person binge? And how often and when, and are the times similar and just what and how does the person feel before the urge or need to binge and how do they feel afterwards?

Many people seem to know that "eating disorders" are treated with serotonergic agents, right? The SSRI's and that clumsy old tricyclic antidepressant Anafranil. The noradrenergic antidepressants are labeled that they are not to be used in "eating disorders" (the lump approach again). In anorexia with such compromised and metabolically imbalanced patients they run a risk of seizures. That's the key. Serotonin. Yep. So why do so many bulimics do so poorly with these drugs. Right, they really don't want to get better. Wrong.

A staggering number of bulimics and binge eaters have a remarkably similar history if one bothers to take it. No surprise, they all binge. But when, on what, and why?

Looking backward as one is forced to do with adult patients with entrenched behavior patterns, maladaptive or not, is to unpeel a stinky onion. It's hard for them to talk about. They feel they are being mocked, or treated gratuitously. No one else ever asked them questions like this before. They just heard "binge" and prescribed an SSRI. And the patient just got agitated and anorgasmic and insomniac and gained weight and felt frustrated and angry and defective and ate some more.

What do these folks eat? Not fats, not proteins, usually not complex carbohydrates. Not whiskey and wine and beer. Nope. Sugar. Simple sugar. As in sugar and cookies and cake and candy and sweets and juices and anything that contains simple, readily absorbed sugar. Sugar. Sugar rush. It perks them up and they feel better and perkier and more alert and happier and less depressed and awake and then guilty and lousy and bad and so forth and so on. By their mid twenties these patterns are so entrenched, ritualized, so much a habit that the individual must stop and think and ponder to begin to identify and express what and how they felt when this began and what it is now that they feel before, during and after.

Careful examination reveals that the urge to binge follows a period of feeling tired and/or depressed and/or lethargic. Sugar perks them up straight away. Zing! And yes. A multitude of them have been tested for diabetes mellitus and for hypoglycemia, but to no avail.

Associated symptoms, if one bothers to ask include a tendency towards moodiness, usually short of major depression. Most are poor sleepers, tired all the time, their sleep is not restorative. Many are restless, tooth grinding sleepers. Many are left-handed. Many were indifferent students, intelligent but easily bored, easily frustrated. Most are anxious. Many will tell that in college they took some speed (amphetamines) and felt pretty mellow and clear and didn't understand what the speed freaks found so wonderful about the stuff and in retrospect they didn't binge and seemed to lose weight and had a normal appetite somehow.

CHAPTER NINETEEN
TAKE TWO ASPIRIN AND CALL ME IN THE MORNING

Well everyone gets headaches. You know, the garden variety tension headache, the grab bag of migraines, the stuffed-up sinus headache, and the fancy mixed vascular-tension headache. That about sums it up. So what else is new? Take two aspirin and call me in the morning. Sure there are nasty exceptions. Brain tumors and infections and hemorrhages and severe high blood pressure and obscure inflammatory diseases can cause headaches. None of these are pertinent to our discussion here. Hopefully you will never get one of these and if you do you find your way to a competent physician who will make the diagnosis promptly and treat properly. Our purview is not as horrible as these, just incredibly miserable. The first list above, the one used by most clinicians, is incomplete. Hence, by default, a substantial number of patients are misdiagnosed and subjected to improper, ineffective, or damaging therapies. Not to split hairs, but to prevent some splitting headaches, we'll look more closely.

What of the usual? How about the common, ordinary, everyday, run of the mill mundane muscle tension headache. That delightful sort when the back of your neck tightens into a knot that seems to pull your shoulder blades and your scalp together and your teeth clench so hard that your jaw hurts all the way up to your temples and your eyes lose focus and everything pounds and tears and grinds and you have to adjust the rear view mirror on the way home because you have shrunken down at least two inches in height from the morning and you know that a bungee cord suspending a hippopotamus from a bridge is relaxed and loose compared to you and heaven help the poor soul who gets in your way today. That's a typical muscle tension headache.

IT **IS** ALL IN YOUR HEAD:
A Monograph on Wellness for the New Millennium

The constant tension headache leads to muscle fatigue. Small muscle fibers tear. Chemicals are released, kinins, that are irritants and provoke inflammation and pain. This state of tension keeps you stuck in a sympathetic nervous condition, which, as we now know, drives up your blood pressure, tightens up your guts, and . . . about the only thing uncertain here is whether or not the tension headaches are a cause of or a result of the hypersympathetic state. Pain is a potent stimulus. The general response is one of increased sympathetic activity. This devolves rapidly into misery.

In this state of arousal and heightened vigilance everything is more noticeable and more irritating. Not painful as it may be in a migraine, but annoying. Simple sounds become awful noises. Normal speech becomes an angry assault. To turn your head, cope with traffic, co-workers or your children only aggravates matters.

Migraine is to headaches what dictators are to freedom; great variety, all bad. Cloaked in many ways, pain the bottom line remains. Common, classic, ocular, hemiplegic, epileptic, abdominal, menstrual and the bastard cousin cluster, all weave their nefarious ways through your head.

Contrary to myth, migraine does afflict children, even small children. Does it affect babies and toddlers? No one can say for sure, but if one looks carefully at the constellation of symptoms, the answer is probably.

What is a migraine? It is a vascular headache. Helpful? No.

Migraine begins with an abrupt vasoconstriction in extra-cranial blood vessels. This diminishes blood flow briefly and causes the aura experienced in classic migraine. Diminished blood flow to the occipital cortex or eyes causes visual disturbances. Diminished blood flow to other areas of the brain may cause numbness or tingling or paralysis or blindness or a seizure. It may occur in cluster headaches as well. The aura may be flashing lights, spots before your eyes, wavy lines, a weird feeling, dizziness, or innumerable other phenomena. This is when you want to take your medicine if you use a rapid acting vasoconstrictor such as the ergots or Immitrex. Why a vasoconstrictor? Because, after the abrupt vasoconstriction that is the first physiologic event of a migraine there is a sudden, massive vasodilatation. The vessels open wide. As they enlarge minute tears occur in the endothelial lining of the vessels (the innermost layer of the vessel). Chemicals are released, again kinins and histamines, which trigger a response by the body to repair the damage. Unfortunately they also trigger a cascade of inflammatory and pain responses. The blood vessels have tiny sensory nerves in them that sense the pain and so do you. There is the pounding, throbbing pain; the nausea and vomiting; the heightened sensitivity to light; sound and touch; and the sharp, fiery, lancinating stabs of pain that wax and wane a bit. Enough? More?

How about the seizures that may be caused by sudden decreases in blood flow. Or the nerve compression caused by the swollen vessels that can cause transient palsy of the third cranial nerve; one side of the face droops and that eye can't focus and drifts down and out. On occasion actual hemiplegia (paralysis of one side of the body) may occur, and sometimes may not resolve. Strokes do occur.

The histamine released causes nasal and sinus blood vessels to become engorged and fills the nose and sinus with mucous. The whole sequence can occur rapidly. This leads to the misdiagnosis of sinus headaches. The number of patients who have had sinus x-rays that come up negative is remarkable.

Migraine tends to occur on one side of the head at a time; hemicranial pain. It may vary from one side to the other. Migraine rarely encompasses the entire head at once. If the pain spreads from one side to the other it usually means that a muscle tension component has been added to the equation. Not to mention the pain engendered by the sinus engorgement. A barrel of laughs.

The body responds to migraine, an internal assault, as it does to an external assault. There is a massive sympathetic response. You should have this memorized by now. Release of adrenaline; heart pounding; muscles tense; alimentary canal seizes and backs up, and so on.

Migraine does run in families. It can occur for no good reason. It can be precipitated by the monthly hormonal and fluid/electrolyte changes of a woman's menstrual cycle, as well as by the less well defined cycles that occur in men (who have regular variations in mood, sleep, gastrointestinal function, fluid retention, etc.).

Migraine sufferers (migraineurs to the unfortunate in group) are not awakened by their headaches. Often they try to go to sleep. Such is not the case with cluster headaches which, if they occur while the individual is asleep, awaken the victim to indescribable pain from which they wish they could by sleeping. The worst complication of cluster headache, by no means rare, is suicide. It hurts that bad.

CLUSTER HEADACHES

Cluster headaches come in clusters. They may be brief; a few days, or a few months. In rare cases they may be chronic. The pattern seems to be distinctive to the individual. They may build slowly and disappear swiftly or start full blown and taper tediously. They may occur many times a day and be totally disabling. Unlike migraine which has a greater prevalence in women than men, cluster has a 90% preponderance in men. It may start in childhood and burn out in later decades of life. These wretched headaches often are precipitated by change in season (they have one of the great eponymic monikers of all time – Horton's Histaminic Cephalalgia). The experience is indistinguishable from migraine, only worse, much worse.

The treatment of migraine has probably caused as many headaches as it has helped, the headaches equally divided between the patients and the doctors. With so many approaches and variations extant, we'll make a list.

1.   Analgesics = pain killers. *A large group. There are the pure pain killers; narcotics, they numb the pain. Aspirin; diminishes pain as well as having an anti-inflammatory effect, which counters the inflammatory aspect of migraine. Non-steroidal anti-inflammatory drugs decrease pain and inflammation as well. Tylenol decreases pain with less effect on inflammation. The side effects of all of these treatments are well known.*

2.   Vasoconstrictors; to decrease the caliber of the massively stretched blood vessels. *These run the gamut from the old standby caffeine which is swift and short acting to the new Imitrex group also swift and short acting to the middle-aged group of ergots which are not as fast as Imitrex, and also short acting. One must take care not to over use these drugs. Too much vasoconstriction is a bad idea. It leads to heart attack, stroke and gangrene.*

3.   Serotonin agents which increase serotonin activity or availability. *The SSRIs are notorious as are some of the older tricyclic antidepressants such as Elavil. Also oddball substances like Sansert are used.*

4.   Anti-Serotonin agents which decrease or block serotonin activity. *Periactin is most notable. It is also a potent antihistaminic.*

5.   Membrane stabilizers, supposedly stabilize the membranes of nerve cells and possibly blood   vessels. *These prevent or stop the cascade of reactions that occur in the headaches. Included in this group are anticonvulsants such as Depakote, Tegretol, and Lamictil*

and others. Lithium and the calcium channel blockers are used as well. From time to time someone benefits from these.

6.	Beta blockers are drugs that block beta sympathetic receptors in the body. *Blockade of these receptors may diminish the vasomotor activity of migraine and prevent the unpleasant cascade's occurrence. Some benefits accrue for a small group.*

7.	Alpha blockers which interfere with alpha adrenergic receptors. *Different chemistry but same concept as with beta blockers.*

8.	Sedatives, calm you down. Maybe if you weren't so high strung you wouldn't get headaches. Or maybe you just need to be knocked down when it happens. *The pain of migraine and cluster drives the sympathetic nervous system in the same way that panic does, with much the same result.*

9.	Combinations or cocktails of drugs. *Midrin and Fiorinal and Excedrin and so forth. A little of this and a little of that and a wish that something in there might do the trick.*

10.	Ice pack. Bring down the swelling and constrict the blood vessels.

11.	Noradrenergic agents to increase noradrenalin. The old Norpramin and the new Wellbutrin, not used enough and sometimes effective.

SINUS HEADACHES

Sinus headaches result from stuffed up sinuses, usually with an aspect of swelling and inflammation of the mucosa (the tissue that lines the sinuses). The former can occur from colds, allergies and obstructions, the latter from colds, allergies and obstructions. Thus there may be a direct pressure effect upon these sensitive tissues as well as the effect of the inflammatory response.

The pain may throb, feel like pressure, hurts behind the eyes,

117

radiates to the temples, about the face, and to the ears. It can be mistaken for migraine or tension. Position change, moving your head about, or trying to get it off the pillow can be an exquisitely excruciating experience. People with hay fever and allergies are vulnerable, although anyone can get a cold, congestion and a sinus headache, with or without an infection.

Acute treatment involves analgesics, decongestants, antihistaminics, and when appropriate, antibiotics. Prophylaxis entails antihistiminics, decongestants, nasally inhaled steroids and sometimes allergy shots. Surgical remedies have been implemented when anatomic problems are contributory; obstructions, polyps, deviated septum, and all the usual excuses for a nose job.

We have described tension, migraine, tension/migraine and sinus headaches. The whole shebang? Nope. Read on.

There remain two more beasts to know. The first is the analgesic rebound headache. In reality there is more to this than just analgesic rebound; there also is vasoconstrictor rebound. This headache often is mistaken for the primary headache pattern, vascular, tension or mixed. It is then treated as the primary headache, which provides brief respite as it fuels and worsens the rebound phenomena.

When a headache happens a significant element of the pain is driven by the inflammatory response. Damaged tissue releases chemicals which cause irritation and inflammation and drive the body's healing response. The inflammation and the chemicals cause pain. Anti-inflammatory drugs block the inflammation, albeit briefly. They do not <u>heal</u> the sore. When these anti-inflammatory medicines, generally short-lived in action wear off, the inflammation and pain <u>rebound</u> with a vengeance as the kinins and other chemicals which have been blocked suddenly are released causing even more pain, which is then treated with another dose of the anti-

inflammatory medicine. The same vicious cycle occurs with analgesics; block the pain perception a while, only for it to rebound as the medicine wears off, and by the vasoconstrictors; shrink the caliber of the blood vessels for a while to decrease the tearing, and the direct pressure effect, only to have a massive rebound of dilatation and the entire cascade of distress as the drug effect wanes.

Therapy for rebound headaches is simple and severe; stop all treatment. Remove all medication as quickly as possible, wait a while for the rebound phenomena to subside, then observe the native headache pattern, diagnose it, and initiate a treatment regimen that lends itself to the avoidance of rebound headaches. Withdrawal must be done properly. Many medicaments used in headache treatment are potentially addictive and can have serious withdrawal consequences. These range from caffeine withdrawal headaches (remember, many headache cocktails contain caffeine), to frank withdrawal seizures and delirium tremens from the several drugs which contain medium acting barbiturates like butabarbital.

Whew! Enough about headaches already? Nope. One more to come. The little known poor relation, the sleep disorder headache.

Have you ever been rousted from a sound, deep sleep, or startled awake just as you were drifting off from light sleep into deeper sleep? How did you feel? Grouchy, irritable and very annoyed might sum it up. What about that sudden, intense, dense, boring headache that drills straight through the center of your forehead, between and behind your eyes and starts to throb and burn and squeeze and you feel meaner than a badger after a root canal.

This headache frequently is mistaken for a migraine. Indeed the qualities of the headache are very much the same as a vascular migraine headache. (*There is little data extant on this variant but I suspect that many of the mechanisms are identical in terms of abrupt vasomotor changes as the brain and body are jarred from a natural rhythm and gears shift suddenly. To be aroused so suddenly necessitates a burst of adrenaline [sympathetic arousal again] with the attendant increases in pulse and blood pressure, muscle tightening and vasoconstriction followed by a compensatory vasodilatation)*

Treatment of the acute headache is similar to that of the typical vascular headache. The critical point here is to understand that this is a different headache from a different source than migraine, amenable to eradication by treatment of the primary sleep problem. Dissection of this headache from migraine and resolution of it helps clear the air about diagnoses, cause and effect, and makes the true migraine much easier to attack successfully. This will be addressed in more depth presently but for the present keep in mind the group of problems we are exploring.

IT **IS** ALL IN YOUR HEAD:
A Monograph on Wellness for the New Millennium

CHAPTER TWENTY
RENEWED VIGOR

Mary suffers from a very severe major depression. The symptoms described are classic and even satisfy DSM IV criteria. Her treatment course is not remarkable. Thousands of patients have been tried on a veritable potpourri of pharmaceuticals, alone and in clumps, only to end up with ECT when all else fails.

ECT in fact is highly effective, much maligned, quite safe, and for the most part underutilized. Is there a problem here?

Yes. Poor Mary has been so ill for so long it's quite a challenge to tease out any other aspect of history and symptomatology other than the depression, the failed treatments, and their side effects.

What is remarkable as we peruse the yard long list of medicaments she has tried thus far is the absence of a pure noradrenergic agent. Indeed a couple of the drugs administered (Tofranil, Remeron, Effexor) have a noradrenergic component but this may be obscured by the combined interference of the undesired serotonergic effects as well as their general side effect profiles.

There are three noradrenergic antidepressants: the elderly Norpramin; the middle aged Ludiomil; and the youngster, Wellbutrin. Additionally the direct stimulants mobilize noradrenalin. These are Dexedrine (noradrenaline and some dopamine, similar to cocaine,), and Ritalin (noradrenaline, dopamine and a bit of serotonin – some people become irritable and dysphoric on Ritalin but not on Dexedrine because they are so sensitive to any increase in serotonergic activity). Sadly it is too common an occurrence to see patients who have had no clean exposure to a noradrenergic medication. Why is something of mystery. Mary might improve with ECT, and if she does the duration of remission is unknown.

IT **IS** ALL IN YOUR HEAD:
A Monograph on Wellness for the New Millennium

Mary is fine and dandy with four weeks of treatment with appropriate doses of Wellbutrin.

FRANK

Frank was so obliterated by Prozac that it took quite awhile for him to be able to realize that he was adrift in la la land most of the time. He did not seem to be terribly depressed anymore. He did not seem to be terribly much of anything anymore. He meandered through life and life went on about him. He was no longer depressed or irritable or upset or angry or happy or sad or eager or horny or anything. He was just there, sort of, most of the time.

Frank's loss of libido troubled his wife. An intelligent man Frank began to wonder in a rather detached manner why it didn't trouble him. Finally at a christening for his first grandchild, a time when everyone else seemed to be happy and elated and overflowing with joy and emotion Frank was very aware that he felt nothing. Some atavistic part of his character asserted itself and he flushed the Prozac and went to see a consultant. It was difficult for Frank to accept that he needed to see a psychiatrist but grudgingly he accepted a referral to a Neuropsychiatrist/Psychopharmacologist.

It took about a month for the Prozac to be metabolized from Frank's system. During that period of time he began a prescription for Wellbutrin SR and Neurontin. Within six weeks he was better than his old self insofar as he was calm and happy with a normal mood range. He experienced the best sleep of his life and had dreams for the first time in some forty five years. His blood pressure was normal without medication and he had no gastrointestinal complaints.

WALLACE

Wallace. Wallace scores high on the Neurosomatic

scale.Look at the list of complaints. Anxiety and panic and headache and stomach and bowels and insomnia. Just a high strung kind of a guy, a worrier, with a tendency to somaticize (or is that somatize?). Certainly an awful lot of autonomic instability.

What is it with Wally? Drives the doctors crazy. One complaint after another. And every drug trial causes more symptoms than it cures. Oh yes, each and every therapist has had his or her formulation as to the neurotic and characterologic and post traumatic and hypochondriacal reasons for Wally's distress as well as his failure to tolerate or respond to all of the treatment offered.

Aha! Wally is an addict, right? He has enormous oral needs that are a manifestation of his not being breast fed and from having been teased because he sucked his thumb especially as he fell asleep until he was five, right? And because he feels okay, in fact normal after a drink or two well obviously he's an alcoholic addict who is drug seeking and will abuse anything he can get his hands on that will give him a buzz which doesn't include all those antidepressants and stomach pills and stuff, right? Which means its immoral and improper and negligent and playing into Wally's hands to give him a prescription for Valium which he is going to abuse and get high on and boost liquor stores and move up to heroin and crack cocaine, right? Wrong. What if you learned that Wally has taken Valium 5 mg twice a day for eighteen years? And he has never been stoned. Along the way he has a social drink and doesn't get drunk. His blood pressure is normal. His stomach and bowels have been fine as has his sleep. He gets a rare migraine. On a particularly stressful day he may get a headache, takes two aspirin and is fine. He doesn't boost convenient stores. He doesn't have the time or the inclination. He's a cardiologist.

JEROME

IT **IS** ALL IN YOUR HEAD:
A Monograph on Wellness for the New Millennium

Jerome has a supposed panic disorder. His panic attacks are fairly typical. But Jerome racks up a lot of points on the Neurosomatic scale. His related complaints include persistent autonomic instability with both upper and lower gastrointestinal disturbances. He has sleep problems, bruxism, variable attention, moodiness and migraine, and mild high blood pressure. He doesn't have good eating habits and snacks all day on cookies and candy. He's had some symptomatic treatment for these individual complaints over time but nothing ever really got better. Predictably an SSRI made him agitated from the start. Norpramin relieved his panic, depression, inattention, migraine, sugar fixes and his blood pressure. The later addition of Neurontin fixed his sleep.

GINA

Gina has a panic disorder correct? Correct. At least by DSM IV criteria. Then why did she not improve on either a serotonergic or noradrenergic medicine. Gosh, she didn't even calm down on Xanax or Klonopin. What seems to be the problem here?

Gina scores right up there on the Neurosomatic scale. Related complaints include depression, migraine, insomnia and GERD. Perhaps she's just a hypochondriac or an hysteric who exaggerates her symptoms as well as the side effects of medication. You know, the kind of person who reads the PDR and searches the Internet to learn every possible adverse reaction to a medication before they try it and then gets most of them, grievously, when they look at the as yet unopened pill bottle newly procured from the pharmacy.

No, Gina's not a fake or an hysteric. Hence she is quite treatable. With a group of medications called the MAO inhibitors (Monoamine oxidase inhibitors). On Parnate she has done beautifully. She's happy and normal and goes about her life (there are only three approved MAOI's in the United States, Parnate, Marplan, and Nardil). These drugs require adherence to a somewhat restricted diet – the avoidance of food and drink that contain the amino acid tyramine because the potential for a severe reaction characterized by sudden high blood pressure. Several medicines and over the counter preparations must be avoided as well. With proper patient education there are rarely any problems and nowadays patients can carry a medication with them to reverse a possible reaction.

But many physicians are not even trained to understand and use these medications so they don't. They don't even think of them. And if they are mentioned by a learned consultant it is not unheard of for a naïve family doctor to mutter something frightful to a patient, a great help to someone who has lost almost all hope.

In more than twenty years I have had five patients experience reactions, none severe, all immediately interdicted by the antidote I gave them with subsequent monitoring in an emergency room for good measure. All were reactions to food. One was caused by a patient's desire to see just how much of a prohibited food she could eat before she had a problem and she found this out brilliantly. The other four were a result of restaurants ignoring precise descriptions from the patients about food additives and preparations.

In Gina's history there are three ways to determine precisely what treatment would and did help Gina. These are not mysterious except to too many prescribers.

Firstly anyone trained with DSM II and/or familiar with the literature of that period would know of the Phobic Anxiety Syndrome (which I encompass in the Neurosomatic Syndrome). This disorder is exquisitely responsive to MAOI's. So from the get go, algorithms notwithstanding, an experienced diagnostician who has seen hundreds or thousands of patients with this problem can comfortably and with assurance recommend an MAOI.

Well and good you say but you don't know phobic anxiety from potatoes and to you panic is panic is panic and that's what the book says now and the algorithm and the approved formulary say Paxil. This leads us to the second clue. When a patient with a panic disorder (and also with some forms of "atypical" depression) seem to begin to respond to several different medicines and in every case after awhile – a few weeks to a few months – medicine seems to lose its effectiveness an MAOI is the treatment of choice and has a very high probability of success.

Ah yes the third clue. This is a psychopharmacological version of the Hail Mary. If everything else has been tried and failed, throw the MAO.

ALLAN

Wasn't it simpler when there was aspirin? Not better, but simpler. For Allan it's neither.

Allan scores admirably on the Neurosomatic scale. His headaches are such a pre-eminent concern that he rarely has the time to complain about his stomach, his bowels, his anxiety or his depression. His blood pressure is elevated as well. But all of these are given short shrift because so much time is taken up with his headaches and the ever changing arsenal of pills. For Allan and his doctors' attempts to separate out side effects from primary complaints long ago became a futile effort.

Competent review of Allan's headache history, general symptoms and pharmacotherapy reveal volumes. Such as? The morning headache the mean frontal central nasty one is a sleep disorder headache. The TMJ is a dead give away. The one sided headaches proceeded by the aura are classic migraine with transient third nerve palsy (Horner's Syndrome) as the swollen blood vessels compress the nerve. These are aggravated by the analgesic rebound phenomenon. The muscle tension headaches are obvious and under the circumstances logical. And by the way the sleep disorder is worsened dramatically by the deleterious effect of SSRI's which worsen alpha intrusion into delta sleep thereby exacerbating rather than ameliorating the problems.

Correction of this mess was long, tedious and painful but worthwhile. SSRI withdrawal with Prozac loading had to be effected and took the expected sixty days to stabilize. The analgesic rebound could be dealt with in only one way; cessation of most of the other medications. During the transition some sedatives were necessary. Ultimately the sleep disorder was corrected with Neurontin; scratch the TMJ and the morning sleep disorder headaches. Once the analgesic rebound resolved the native migraine pattern could be established. Wellbutrin was begun for the headaches as well as to help the anxiety and depression. Periactin a serotonin blocker was begun and the migraines were almost eradicated. The occasional acute headache was treated with Excedrin, sometimes supplemented with a Valium. Muscle tension headaches became rare, situationally related, and treated with a simple analgesic and a change in lifestyle. The autonomic lability resolved as well.

BETTY

Betty's distress was readily apparent. Her primary complaints of headache, jaw pain, exhaustion, anxiety, irritability, forgetfulness and the like were only magnified dramatically by her loss of libido, weight gain, horrible self image and concerns about her marriage.

It took some time but over a period of several weeks Betty was able to be removed carefully from all of her medication. As expected her sleep was dreadful, her jaw hurt, her headaches were frequent and painful, and her outlook grim.

Initially Wellbutrin was prescribed but she found it too stimulating. In its place Ludiomil was begun. She continued to experience poor quality sleep with morning headaches and a sore jaw. A low dose of Klonopin was prescribed every evening. Within a matter of weeks there has been complete resolution of Betty's sleep problems and purported TMJ syndrome. Her headache frequency and intensity has diminished by greater than 85%. She continues to have a monthly menstrual migraine that is rather unpleasant and requires acute intervention but besides that one single occurrence there are no other difficulties.

Over a period of some six months Betty has been able to lose the weight she gained on the original prescriptions. Her libido has returned to normal and her appetite is stable. Marital problems are no longer a concern.

LASZLO

In Laszlo's own words, what's the bottom line here? ADHD Laszlo, at least from the DSM IV perspective, you have ADHD. That's the bottom line Laszlo. Oh yes, you actually have the Neurosomatic Syndrome. You have migraine, ulcer and irritable bowel symptoms, and a sleep disorder to beat the band. But the most prominent manifestation of the Neurosomatic Syndrome in your case is a ADHD.

Pay attention Laszlo. Sit still for four minutes, keep your mouth shut and listen to this. Like hordes of other intelligent people you cruised through school on intellect and will power, usually bored stiff and fantasizing furiously, driven nuts by bureaucrats, pedants and the self proclaimed cool in-group who seemed joined at the hip and always put you down (except when they wanted something) and for years you thought of yourself as stupid, defective, weird or nerdy. Unconsciously developed compensatory strategies helped and hurt at the same time.

Don't argue with me Laszlo I'm the expert here and I know what I am talking about and don't fiddle with my stethoscope. You don't have to bounce off walls to have ADHD and no you do not outgrow it. It is just one facet of the Neurosomatic Syndrome. Yes I agree that it is terribly misdiagnosed, mismanaged and misunderstood. Except I know how to diagnose, manage and treat it.

Yep. Ritalin might help. Or Wellbutrin or maybe Norpramin or Ludiomil. No no no no no, no Prozac. You would be miserable and yes probably impotent. In any case Laszlo, you have to treat the sleep disorder or get used to sleeping alone.

What's the bottom line Laszlo? Adderall 20 mg three times a day and Neurontin 900 mg every evening. Have a nice day.

WHITNEY

When first seen Whitney was an unhappy young lady. Chubby and gloomy and failing in school. She no longer had emotional outbursts. She no longer had emotions. She was tired, exhausted to be more precise. She couldn't much tell her sleep from being awake.

After careful explanations and a tedious removal from her regimen Whitney was begun on a simple regimen, Ritalin 20 mg three times a day. Her response was immediate and dramatic. She continues to have some difficulty with her sleep. There also is a component of a delayed sleep phase disorder, something common in adolescents, as well as periodic limb movement disorder but Whitney's parents wish to defer the use of a GABA ergic drug for the sleep disorder for the present.

IT **IS** ALL IN YOUR HEAD:
A Monograph on Wellness for the New Millennium

LEONARD

Leonard disposed of his symptoms and distress and most of his pharmacy bill when he became stabilized on a noradrenergic antidepressant, Norpramin and a regular daily dose of Valium. He had begun on Klonopin and it worked fine but he developed easy bruising and wanted to see a hematologist because he was sure he had leukemia. His physician knew that this was a possible side effect of Klonopin and offered him Librium or Valium instead of it. Leonard chose Valium because Librium reminded him of Librax! Remember we are treating the Neurosomatic part of his problem here not the neurotic part.

ROBERT

It took awhile for Robert to get straightened out. He was exceedingly unhappy at the idea of a referral to a psychiatrist. He moaned and groaned and complained and was basically very offended and very threatened at the notion. Ultimately however he was able to work with the consultant and ended up on a very simple regime of a noradrenergic antidepressant Wellbutrin; Neurontin during the day for anxiety and in the evening to correct his sleep, and a small dose of Ritalin to fix his attention. He has had no problems subsequently with elevated blood pressure, irritable bowels, or ulcers. Infrequent headaches are treated simply. He was transmogrified from an uninsurable walking pharmaceutical display to a regular guy.

INEZ

Unlike Robert, Inez was eager to be helped. She was thoroughly convinced that whatever it was that ailed her was not in her head in the colloquial sense but was a real illness but at the same time was willing to work with anybody who might have a forthright chance at helping her. Willingly she came off of her old medication and was stabilized, as were so many other patients, on a very simple regimen of a noradrenergic antidepressant Wellbutrin and a GABA ergic drug Neurontin.

TIFFANY

Tiffany presented with classic Neurosomatic symptoms. She also presented with a classic treatment history. Unfortunately her treatment course was difficult, complicated by a multiplicity of side effects.

Tiffany turned out to be allergic to Wellbutrin. She fainted on Norpramin. She then developed a rash on Ludiomil. Not to worry. She began Ritalin three times a day in an appropriate dose. There was an immediate and gratifying response. Her appetite normalized, it did not go away. Her intestinal symptoms and headaches diminished. Her concentration and attention improved and she began to lose weight. She ate regularly and normally and in reasonable quantities. Her "compulsive" sugar cravings disappeared and close upon that so did her "bulimia". Since she no longer "binged" she no longer "purged".

Tiffany also had substantive improvement in her sleep. She did try Neurontin and Klonopin and found that both worked but she thought she felt a bit groggy in the morning. At this point in time Tiffany feels that her sleep is satisfactory and she is dramatically improved in all spheres.

It is important to note that her appetite is now modulated not suppressed.

BERT

Bert was uncomfortable seeing a psychiatrist. After the remark made by his physician friend he was desperately afraid that a psychiatrist would think he was a latent homosexual because he seemed to have some sort of eating disorder.

Not to worry it's a Neurosomatic problem. All the pieces fit together.

With his consent Bert was removed carefully from all of his previous medication with appropriate monitoring. He began a regimen of Wellbutrin. There was rapid and gratifying impact on his appetite, eating, gastrointestinal function, anxiety and sensitive stomach. His attention seemed to be better as well. His sleep however was lousy.

Neurontin did correct Bert's sleep swiftly with anticipated rebound effects. However in Bert's case this was undesirable because it seemed to cause some erectile dysfunction. At first Bert thought that this was another sign of some sexual identity problem but was reassured to know that it was just the medication side effect. Transferred to Valium he has done well ever since.

MAUREEN

Maureen has supposed fibromyalgia. Fibromyalgia has become a very en vogue diagnosis. It leads to much dispute. Many doctors don't believe there is such a thing. Others say there is but don't know exactly what it is. Clearly it is a syndrome or part of a syndrome.

Within the context of the Neurosomatic Syndrome it becomes readily understood.. Maureen's history and Neurosomatic score are totally supportive of the diagnosis. As with many patients her age she has had prior diagnoses such as chronic fatigue syndrome, hypoglycemia and panic disorder. In fact she has had the same thing all the time. It's just that different facets of the problem, different symptoms, achieved prominence at different times. Gradually Maureen was removed from her regimen that was a bit of this and a bit of that. She experienced some unpleasant rebound insomnia and this was to be expected. She was significantly depressed and relatively anxious at the time her new treatment began hence she was started on an appropriate dose of Wellbutrin for a woman. Neurontin was begun in the evening. As anticipated she experienced delta and REM rebound but after two to three weeks had complete resolution of all of her symptoms. She slept well and deeply with dreams and muscle relaxation. Her aches and pains and sore joints and sore jaw resolved. She no longer required a dental apparatus when she slept. She became active and involved in her life again.

Because her mood improved and her anxiety diminished after a period of time Maureen chose to taper off the Wellbutrin and continue on the Neurontin alone. She did very, very well.

As with many people with this set of problems Maureen notes that if she does not take the Neurontin as prescribed she reverts immediately to her native and lousy sleep pattern.

CRAIG

When first seen in consultation Craig was angry, miserable, a bit belligerent and highly skeptical. He had been through the mill of consultants and felt he was no better off than when he started other than now he was taking a variety of medications that seemed to cause a variety of side effect problems, most particularly lethargy on top of his exhaustion.

Tediously Craig was removed from his previous pharmacotherapeutic regimen. As is always the case in such situations unavoidable hypnotic rebound occurred. Always inquisitive and "compulsive" Craig searched the internet and the libraries in search of data about the Neurosomatic Syndrome. He found none. He did find a wealth of information about ADHD and irritable bowel syndrome and migraine and sleep disorders and anxiety disorders and medication. Able to correlate anecdotal data with facility he began to see the concept of Neurosomatics. He also understood that he had had prominent attentional and sleep symptoms throughout life.

Initially reluctant but then enthusiastic Craig embarked upon a new treatment program. The initial prescriptions were for Wellbutrin and Neurontin with dramatic results. However Craig found that Wellbutrin was not quite sufficient for improving his attentional problems. Gradual introduction of Ritalin caused him to become irritable and dysphoric, this from the serotonergic boost caused by Ritalin. Switched to Dexedrine in appropriate doses he has done extremely well without an antidepressant and with appropriate doses of Neurontin in the evening.

Craig is one of the luckier individuals insofar as he has found that if he takes Neurontin regularly for three or four months and corrects his sleep he seems able to come off of it for variable periods of time. He can go generally for two to four months before his sleep will begin to deteriorate and as soon as it does he resumes Neurontin for a period of time. The misinterpretation of Craig's sleep study is classic and characteristic of the misunderstanding of Neurosomatics and purported fibromyalgia. The initial interpreter's analysis of Craig's study was teleologic in nature. This means that the observed phenomenological results, the alpha intrusion and prolonged REM latencies are seen to be a result and meaning to explain a phenomenon. Through the looking glass, from a biophysiologic perspective, we come to understand that the prolonged REM latencies and alpha delta sleep in fact are manifestations of the core problem, the sleep disorder of the Neurosomatic Syndrome as manifest by periodic limb movement disorder. The restlessness, bruxism, anxiety, depression, irritability, aches, pains and everything else are the result.

RACHAEL

Rachael did not suffer from the Neurosomatic Syndrome. Nor did she suffer from any other biologically based depression, anxiety, or what have you. Rachael, as did millions of other people at some time in their lives had a period of emotional turmoil, ambivalence, uncertainty and fear. Done with college and facing adult life she was scared. Not depressed. Yet a ten or fifteen minute visit with a family practitioner who hardly knew her led to a prescription for a mind numbing SSRI and years of drifting through life and into a marriage she couldn't understand when detoxified from the SSRI. Her story is not uncommon.

CHAPTER TWENTY ONE
THE BAD NEWS

We have now re-reviewed the symptoms, diagnoses and treatments of our patients. Within the concept and context of the Neurosomatic Syndrome, be it the problem list identified on page 3, or the chart above on page 15 it seems that there are vast numbers of people who are afflicted with symptoms of the Neurosomatic Syndrome. This is not to state or imply that everyone with panic or anxiety or depression or headaches or fitful sleep has this but it does suggest that individuals who have a sufficient number of symptoms do have it.

Having understood and accepted the concept the treatment then becomes rather simple. From long lists of polypharmaceutical regimens and unacceptable amounts of SSRI's these patients seem to be well treated, stable, comfortable, and satisfied with small amounts of a very short list of drugs. Is this some kind of panacea or magic bullet? No. It remains that there is available a relatively short list of drugs that attack the central problem of the Neurosomatic Syndrome. This will change in the coming years as more noradrenergic medications are developed but the list is rather limited at this time.

But what of the present treatment. Supposed state of the art medicine, treatment algorithms, and pharmaceutical advertising trumpets the magical benefits of SSRI's, the mainstay of treatment for most of <u>individual symptoms</u> of the Neurosomatic Syndrome. This is the case despite facts, evidence, and logic. It matters not that the medical literature has disclosed a remarkable coincidence or co-morbidity of irritable bowel syndrome in some patients with depression and that such patients should not be treated with serotonergic medications but with a noradrenergic drug. It matters not that there is an abundance of literature on biogenic amines in depression that goes back at least to the late 1960's that delineates clearly between noradrenergic and serotonergic depressions and the treatments thereof. SSRI's remain today's Novocain for the brain, snake oil for the twenty first century.

It is necessary at this time to devolve into a discussion of these medications and their Neuropsychiatric and physiologic effects so that we may understand proper and effective treatment as opposed to improper symptom suppression

CHAPTER TWENTY TWO
HISTORICAL NOTES AND ANECDOTES
GOOF BALLS

The author Kurt Vonnegut, Jr. wrote a short story called "Welcome to the Monkey House". In it he describes an overpopulated society where everyone is required by law to take a pill – a pill originally developed to control the wanton behavior of the zoo monkeys which offended the sensibility of some – which eradicated all sexual urge or desire, effectively rendering everyone numb from the waist down. The result is a society of numb nut numbskulls. There is of course a guerrilla revolutionary movement that is for sex. Please read the story. More to follow.

IT **IS** ALL IN YOUR HEAD:
A Monograph on Wellness for the New Millennium

CHAPTER TWENTY THREE
SARAH TONEN AND POLLY FARMACI

The time has come to talk about the evil sisters serotonin and polypharmacy. Why related and why evil? Firstly the national obsession with serotonin has led both to a misunderstanding of fundamental and sophisticated neuropsychophamacology and an over prescription of serotonergic drugs. Secondly and in large measure because of this polypharmacy has increased exponentially, again for two basic reasons. One is the failure to diagnose and treat correctly which fosters abundant over prescription, often shotgun prescribing to try to find something that works. The other is the need to treat the many horrible side effects induced by the initial treatment, many of them misdiagnosed as primary illnesses.

Serotonin is not the only transmitter in your brain. You wouldn't know that if you read many medical journals today. Serotonin is implicated in everything that may have any connection to the nervous system. There are fancy if incomprehensible drawings of serotonin receptors and sub-serotonin receptors in articles about the importance of serotonin in almost everything from anxiety to zoophilia. And in at least 99% of these references the drugs of choice are the SSRI's.

The SSRI's are marketed furiously. For years many medical journals have been supported by SSRI advertising. It may sound cynical but it remains a fact that these same journals that are basically paid for by advertising from the manufacturers of SSRI's have been painfully tardy in the publication of any letters or articles critical of SSRI's or contrary to the present major preoccupation with them.

More recently the manufacturers have begun direct marketing to the public with television commercials that advertise the remark able benefits of these medications for everything that ails you; social anxiety, obsessive compulsive disorder, depression, and a variety of other ailments. These commercials are a throw back to the snake oil salesmen of the 19th and early 20th century.

The SSRI's are the serotonin selective re-uptake inhibitors. Putatively they block the re-uptake or resorption of the transmitter serotonin by the releasing nerve cell or neuron, the neuron sending the message. In so doing the serotonin is available longer to the receiving neuron, the neuron receiving the message. Since it's there longer, it works longer, effectively increasing the effect. Sounds simple enough so far. What's the problem?

The answer again is twofold. One: if you <u>don't need</u> more serotonin in the first place, if your serotonin system is just fine and dandy and all of a sudden you get a whole bunch more is there an effect? Does it make you even more depressed; does it make you more than manic; does it make you ill in some other ways?

Two: the SSRI's affect more than serotonin. They also induce significant dopamine blockade. And this is a very serious problem.

Whoa! Wait a minute. What's this with dopamine, aren't we here to discuss serotonin? Yes, but we can't avoid it because these drugs mess up dopamine. The six SSRI's commonly used in the United States are Prozac, Zoloft, Paxil, Effexor, Luvox, and Celexa. All are potent dopamine blockers.

Dopamine. What does it do? Let's examine three major examples. In Paralysis Agitans or Parkinson's Disease to use the eponym, it is dopamine producing neurons that are lost. This leads to a loss of homeostasis, an imbalance between the dopaminergic and cholinergic neurons. The cardinal symptoms are loss of spontaneous motion and expression, rigidity, tremors, depression, and an internal sense of distress and dysphoria. It's as if you want to move but can't, or as if no matter what you do you can't get comfortable.

In cocaine abuse and addiction two neurotransmitters are released abruptly; noradrenalin and dopamine. It is important to know that dopamine release is a key element to the high, the good feeling obtained. In schizophrenia the mainstay of treatment is with medications that block dopamine. Dopamine blockades suppresses many of the devastating symptoms of schizophrenia. It also causes a myriad of terrible side effects. These include drug induced pseudo-Parkinsonism, as well as a clutch of dreadful Tardive processes; Tardive dyskinesia, Tardive akathisia, Tardive parkinsonism, Tardive dystonia, and Tardive Tourette's and their repulsive cousins, withdrawal dyskinesias.

Tardive means tardy or late in onset. This means that after taking one of the dopamine blocking drugs for awhile, symptoms begin to re-emerge. There are theories about super sensitization of dopamine receptors and such like but they are beyond our present concerns. What emerges are groups of miserable symptoms. The dyskinesias are characterized by continuous muscle twitches and jerks and spasms. Often these involve the mouth and tongue and are very obvious and disfiguring. However the entire body may be affected; neck, trunk and extremities. If you have ever seen it you understand. In rare cases the esophagus can be involved and make swallowing impossible. In other cases the diaphragm becomes affected and breathing is compromised.

Tardive akathisia is less overt. It is a sense of restlessness, a need to move, an inability to rest or be still and comfortable. It is accompanied by a wretched sense of subjective dysphoria, a horrible feeling of internal pain/anxiety/angst/distress/misery. People have described it in the same words over and over; they feel like they want to crawl out of their skin. They don't know whether to scream or cry or go berserk.   One person's simile was to say it was as if a company of marines in concert were scratching their fingernails across a blackboard!

These Tardive processes break through after awhile.   If the dosage of the dopamine blocking drug is increased the Tardive process is suppressed – but only for awhile.   Eventually the Tardive process breaks through again.   This is called tachyphylaxis.   This endless spiral continues.   There is a limit to the amount of medication that can be prescribed; there is no limit to the breakthrough.   It's a losing battle.

Additionally the Tardive processes can occur with the cessation of dopamine blockade therapy.   Abrupt termination or rapid attenuation of treatment increases the risk of a Tardive process.   But there is no way to guarantee this won't happen.

There are several points of information relative to the occurrence of the neurotoxic Tardive processes.   Tardive processes are much more likely to occur in patients with affective disorders or problems other than schizophrenia.   Also Tardive processes are more likely to occur with pulse exposure to the offending agents than with continuous exposure.   The two sides of this reveal that experienced psychopharmacologists are loathe to use such drugs in affective disorders unless they are absolutely, positively necessary and that patients with affective disorders are much more likely to require and receive brief pulse exposures than are unfortunate schizophrenics.

Withdrawal dyskinesias, as alluded to above have the same range and symptoms as their Tardive cousins except that they occur upon the withdrawal of the offending agent.   As with Tardive processes these are miserable and may be permanent.

These problems can be caused by drugs other than dopamine blocking anti-psychotic drugs (also called neuroleptics because they can cause neurologic damage). Compazine an anti-nausea drug, and Reglan a gastrointestinal drug have the same risks. **_SO DO THE SSRI'S._**

Millions if not a billion or two have been spent to push the SSRI's. They are detailed intensely (hawked by pharmaceutical company reps) to family doctors, internists, pediatricians, obstetrician gynecologists, nurse practitioners and physicians assistants. "Unrestricted" research grants are awarded to institutions where notable "lead investigators" just happened to end up doing studies that support the use of these drugs for, well, just about everything under the sun. Price wars between manufacturers foster deals with HMO's and managed care organizations to get one or another SSRI as the "approved" first choice drug on the formulary, in some cases the only approved drug.

Thus the SSRI's are widely (over) prescribed. Grudgingly over the past several years, and after many of us knew the truth, articles appeared about: augmentation of SSRI's with Wellbutrin or Ritalin. Query: Are these "augmenting agents" improving the salutary effects of the SSRI, treating the side effects of the SSRI, or treating the primary illness which was not treated successfully or was in fact worsened by the SSRI? And, treatment of SSRI induced sexual dysfunction with many agents including Ritalin and Wellbutrin. While adverse "extra pyramidal" reactions to all of the SSRI's (the Tardive and pseudo parkinsonian reactions noted above) had been reported for many years such reports got into journals very slowly and not until 1998 were SSRI withdrawal syndromes acknowledged in the literature in a meaningful way. And then in a limited manner.

In the case examples in this book we see many examples of polypharmacy, often a result of multiple prescriptions from multiple physicians. This is one form of polypharmacy. How about the other?

In psychiatry for at least three decades as psychopharmacology has evolved a basic tenet of it has been to use the smallest amount of the fewest medications possible. Whatever the problem, the disease, the disorder, the use of multiple drugs has been anathema. But lately and quite precisely since the advent of the SSRI's a body of literature has developed "in defense of polypharmacy". It is worrisome and pathetic and reveals profound ignorance and narrow mindedness on the part of the supposed authorities. This is not to state or imply that mono therapy, a single drug therapy is always feasible, but it is scary when a correct diagnostic formulation is not achieved and then a fusillade of drugs is fired broad side at a patient to "treat" the initial complaints, the iatrogenic (treatment induced) complaints, the side effects, and the "undesirable" personality characteristics of an individual, plus the treatment of the side effects of the drug used to treat the first wave of side effects, let alone the unidentified withdrawal symptoms from a recently discarded drug. This does not begin to address the other organ system problems that have been missed and probably exacerbated by the inappropriate treatment.

If you get more than one psychoactive drug from a non-psychiatrist, panic and demand to see a Neuropsychiatrist or Psychopharmacologist. If a supposed specialist begins to give you a pile of drugs all at once, or in rapid sequence with a mind boggling song and dance that you need a pinch of this for your D2 receptor and a smidge of that for your 5 HT receptors and a dram of whatever for your serotonin level and a sprinkle of the other for good measure start to think about eye of Newt, toads, and bubbling cauldrons and get the heck out of there and find someone who can tell up from down without having to drop something to be sure.

medication the quantity of sleep may increase but the quality is poor and deteriorates. Hence the patient remains chronically sleep deprived with all of the sequelae of that problem.

On initiation of SSRI therapy many patients experience gastrointestinal distress. This runs the gamut from nausea and vomiting to heartburn to cramps to diarrhea. These may decrease over time. These symptoms are treated with the full range of GI drugs. Antacids, H2 blockers, HCL inhibitors, anticholinergic/antispasmodic drugs, sedatives, reglan and more. And of course each and everyone of these drugs may induce another wave of side effects. Don't these myriad intestinal complaints mirror identically those in our previous discussion of Neurosomatic gastrointestinal problems?

While some patients indeed experience a decrease in migraine headaches on an SSRI a significant number suffer a worsening of the headaches. And others who have never had migraines suffer it for the first time on SSRI's. Many experience an onset or intensification of painful frontal headaches with which they awaken every morning. Again these are sleep disorder headaches misdiagnosed as migraine. .

Individuals with true Anorexia Nervosa can do well on proper doses of SSRI's in conjunction with a coherent treatment plan for that difficult disease. Medical, metabolic, dietary and psychotherapeutic interventions are all a necessary part of the treatment. Other eating disorders, bulimia, bingeing and the like are not so well treated with the SSRI's. Many patients find that as they are numbed by the drug and feel less and less that they may binge less frequently but instead they just plain overeat. Weight gain on an SSRI if you are not anorexic or if it is not the recovery to normal body weight of the loss engendered by a depression is a very bad sign. This particular side effect is not typically treated with drugs but instead with the old saw, "don't eat so much"

    "Fibromyalgia" in most cases is really a result of alpha delta sleep. Some symptoms of "fibromyalgia" may decrease in a portion of patients treated with SSRI's but the disruptive effect on sleep usually is worse than any benefit achieved. The treatment of fibromyalgia as it stands is such a hodgepodge that anything that complicates it is a bad idea. Multi drug regimens are common as are frequent changes in treatment.

CHAPTER TWENTY FOUR
BIPOLAR TOO!

Depression, or major depression as it is now known is also called a unipolar mood disorder. It has one direction, down. DSM IV is not internally consistent for in its eagerness to rename everything it left depression but eradicated manic depressive illness. That no longer exists. Even if you are Vincent Van Gogh you can't be manic depressive in America. But you can be bipolar. Isn't that a relief? Whew! Almost couldn't be sick there for a minute. Bipolar means two poles, up and down.

Not only can you be bipolar but you have several flavors. Bipolar I is as you may have guessed classic manic depressive illness. This is characterized by severe mood swings, very high and at times very low, sometimes with psychotic features (loss of touch with reality). Bipolar III is an odd variant with manic ups but no depressions. It is not common. There has been some talk of a bipolar IV but no one has any real idea of what it's supposed to be which means that someone is on the verge of trying to rename everything again. And there is Bipolar II.

Bipolar II is a most subtle form of this illness. It is difficult to diagnose. It is often missed. It is usually over treated. What is it?

Bipolar II is a cyclic mood disorder of ups and downs. The ups are quite brief and quite mild. They may last anywhere from an hour or two to a few days. They are not wild and crazy. They are a bit exuberant, a tad over the top. A little giddy, a little loud, maybe too much energy and a bunch of good ideas, projects to do. Maybe spend a bit too much. This mild hypomania fizzles abruptly often if an insult or rejection occurs, and there follows a rapid crash into depression that may be mild to moderately severe. The depression tends to last longer than the hypomania and can be quite miserable.

The cycles may be occasional or frequent, even several times a week. This is called rapid cycling. The difficulty in the treatment of Bipolar II is that while the mood variations can be treated with all of the usual medications used in bipolar mood disorders, eradication of some cycling is not possible. On the one hand everybody has mood variations so it is rather hard to say when the variations are within or without a normal range. On the other hand attempts to establish a "normal mood" is regularly misunderstood and aims for a flat line with no variation. The result of this is gross over medication and near stupor plus a satchel full of side effects from the likes of lithium, other mood stabilizers, and the widely over prescribed Depakote (talk about weight gain, talk about Depakote).

Now that you know more about mood disorders than most therapists, we can proceed with our sack of the SSRI's. On to anxiety and depression.

The incidence of bipolar diagnoses in general and of both type I and type II specifically have increased dramatically over the past ten years. There may be several possible reasons for this. These would include a better understanding of the illness, greater diagnostic acumen, an actual increase in occurrence and several other factors. Curiously enough this is the same period of time in which the SSRI's were introduced to America, pushed like manna, and virtually exploded throughout the country. Is this a coincidence? Maybe. Maybe not.

A very peculiar thing happens to an astounding number of people who are treated for supposed depression and/or anxiety with SSRI's. They find out that they are bipolar. They never were before. They never had mood swings of the type described above. Oh, they had good times and they had bad times but they never had a manic episode before. To be sure some of them may have been bipolar II and never knew. And maybe some of them had a proclivity to bipolar illness but hadn't had a first manic episode yet (a debate has meandered about the literature for years as to whether or not antidepressants can precipitate mania in either of two ways; one is to provoke mania from a quiescent state in a true bipolar patient who had had or who had not yet had a manic episode; the other is to cause a drug induced mania in a patient who otherwise did not have and would not have mania except for the effects of the drug and would no longer have it if the offending agent were removed).

Obviously these bipolar patients need some anti-manic mood stabilizing medication to correct this problem. It would appear that the antidepressant SSRI did alleviate the depression because the patient is now manic, often very manic, often very very manic and agitated and wild and aggressive and out of control and certainly needs something (actually some patients can have mixed bipolar symptoms with simultaneously manic and depressed symptoms). Prescriptions then abound for Lithium, Depakote, Tegretol, Neurontin, Klonopin and other sedatives, and also for the anti-psychotic, neuroleptic major tranquilizers. And each and every medication has its own bag of potential side effects. And then these side effects must be addressed often with changes in regimens or the addition of more medications.

No. I do not assert that everyone treated with an SSRI becomes bipolar. Nor do I assert that SSRI's always cause mania, either primary (patient is bipolar) or secondary (drug induced in a patient otherwise not bipolar). However if you received the diagnosis of bipolar illness after treatment with an SSRI some careful introspection and reconsideration is warranted. Let's examine this more closely.

Many patients present with complaints of depression and anxiety are begun on SSRI's. Most often these prescriptions are not written by psychiatrists – this doesn't leave psychiatrists off the hook because most of them do the same thing. Most patients receive SSRI's. HMO drug formularies and depression treatment algorithms usually direct this. Not a lot of thought seems to go into these prescriptions. The SSRI's are considered pretty safe, not addictive drugs. So what the heck. Thus children and adolescents and adults and seniors get an SSRI with ease, usually in brief ten or fifteen minute office visit from someone who is not a specialist in psychiatric diagnosis or in psychopharmacology and who has absolutely no idea of what these drugs might do other than something or other to your serotonin and that they're supposed to be very simple to use and don't have very many side effects.

CHAPTER TWENTY FIVE
BANANAS

As you may have guessed a whole lot of people have side effects from these SSRI's that are not identified correctly for what they are, with tragic results. Above we have explored the headaches, sleep and gastrointestinal problems that often occur. And we have mentioned the problem of being numbed out which will be expanded upon below. We have alluded to the issue of bipolar illness. What of it? There are three major aspects of this problem.

One relates to agitation and over stimulation by these drugs in people who should not be on them. Another involves the intense and horrible withdrawal syndrome that can occur, is rarely identified for what it is, is misinterpreted, and not properly treated. Finally, with contributions from both of the above, concerns the ramifications of these reactions in children, adolescents, and individuals with certain character pathology.

Here's the low down. If you are treated with an SSRI and you have no perceptible problems when you begin on it, and if after three to four weeks you are pretty much back to normal and you still have no problems and you have a normal range of mood and affect and sleep and appetite and you can experience joy and you can experience sadness and you can be happy and you can be angry and you can laugh and you can cry and you can look forward with eager anticipation to good thinks and you are your old self, whomever that happens to be, then it looks like you lucked out and you are on the right medicine and should continue to do well if you follow a good treatment plan.

However if you began an SSRI and within a dose or two you felt intensely anxious, agitated, restless, as if you couldn't sit still or as if you wanted to crawl out of your skin and thought you were going to lose control of yourself or just plain lose your mind, but your doctor told you just to ride it out and it would go away or gave you another prescription for some sort of sedative or tranquilizer, or determined that obviously you were bipolar and began you on Depakote or another marvelous mood stabilizer – you were on the wrong drug!

The intensely miserable feelings experienced are in part an acute adverse reaction to the dopamine blockade caused by the SSRI as it induces acute akathisia (physical restlessness and subjective dysphoria), in conjunction with an acute reaction to unnecessary and excessive serotonin; effectively a mild acute serotonin syndrome. We haven't mentioned this serotonin syndrome before. (The serotonin syndrome is a dangerous phenomenon that occurs from too much serotonin or too much serotonin activity. It is characterized by agitation, flushing, autonomic lability, changes in mental status and several other bad things. The intensity of distress and dysphoria varies from person to person.) Children and adolescents may escalate wildly out of control all of sudden, in rage or anger or crying or violence. They may become dangerous to self or others and once their toxic drug screens come back clean they become bipolar, too. Individuals with primitive, infantile character pathology who don't happen to need more serotonin often behave as the description implies as do the kids.

154

CHAPTER TWENTY SIX
THE MONKEY ON YOUR BACK

For several years an SSRI withdrawal syndrome has been identified and treated by some clinicians. Yet tediously, over the years, in the face of pertinacious resistance reports of this squeaked into the literature. Real acknowledgment of this phenomenon did not gain mainstream acceptance until 1998. The literature thus far dramatically underestimates the frequency and severity of the problem and has tried to come up with a simple minded treatment for it (algorithm in the making).

To this date several drug companies advertise and market their SSRIs on Television and in magazines and continue to state-- falsely--that these drugs are not habit forming and do not have withdrawal syndromes. The same marketing (detailing) is done by pharmaceutical reps daily in your doctor's office.

Before we describe the withdrawal syndrome and its treatment we need to do another basic science update. *The SSRI's Paxil, Effexor, Luvox, Zoloft, and Celexa all have a short half life of approximately five days. This means that in five days one half of the drug in your system has been metabolized (digested) by your body and excreted (removed). Of the five Paxil is far and away the most potent of the drugs. It is much stronger per milligram than the others. Hence as it swiftly goes away the withdrawal effects tend to occur more quickly and viciously although all of these rapidly metabolized drugs swiftly cause distress. Prozac is an incredibly long acting drug and has metabolic by-products with half lives of four weeks or more. If there is anything good to say about Prozac it is that it self tapers. It goes away very slowly and without the withdrawal problems of the others. Nonetheless it can cause all of the same front and back end adverse problems and reactions as the other SSRI's.*

Withdrawal reactions from the SSRI's can occur if one dose of the shorter acting drugs is missed. Awful misery can occur if a patient misses a single day's dose of Paxil. The same can be said for Luvox and Zoloft and Celexa although it may take a day or two longer for all hell to break loose. A major complicating variable is that many, many patients end up on ridiculously high doses of SSRI's. Thus it is all too common to see patients in particular young adolescents on 60 mg per day of Paxil , or 200 mg per day of Zoloft, or 300 mg per day of Luvox. So when they miss a dose the biochemical effects in their nervous system are profound and not salutary.

And what happens in SSRI withdrawal? There is significant autonomic lability. Pulse and respiration vary and there is flushing and intense gastrointestinal activity; cramps, nausea, diarrhea, vomiting (hey, wait a moment, haven't we discussed the autonomic nervous system before?!). There is dizziness, headaches, and a very spacey feeling. There is intense restlessness. The words of dozens of patients have been identical: "I felt I wanted to crawl out of my skin." Heart pounding, tightness in the chest, skin crawling and an absolute inability to sleep. Many believe that they are losing their minds. Most believe that they are losing control and in fact many do, especially the younger ones who go off like grenades. Persistent, disturbing uncontrollable crying is common.

I have seen an unfortunate series of young adolescents who have become so wild and violent so suddenly that police have to be summoned. Of course if the wrong "professionals" get involved these kids are diagnosed as manic, psychotic, borderline, oppositional, intoxicated, dissociative, or victims of abuse, with the "correct" intervention and treatment for such problems vigorously imposed.

Remember these reactions can occur if just one dose of

medicine is missed, especially with Paxil. Some journal wonks have suggested that SSRI withdrawal may occur only if a person has been on the medication for several months. This is not true. Withdrawal reactions can occur after only a few doses of the medicine.

Pathetically these withdrawal phenomena are interpreted by many prescribers to be proof of the patients need for the medication. If you miss a dose or two and all of your symptoms come back in rush, it's proof positive of the rectitude of the diagnosis and the need for treatment to continue.

While I believe the front end problems of the SSRIs to be caused by a combination of dopamine blockade and serotonin excess, the withdrawal reactions are almost certainly a result of the sudden release of dopamine blockade by these drugs. This amounts to an hyper acute withdrawal akathisia and dyskinesia. Recall if you will that the anti-psychotic neuroleptic drugs do the same thing. However those drugs all have much longer half lives. They stick around longer after they are stopped. But these SSRIs have a short half life. Their levels in the body plummet and the dopamine blockade suddenly ceases. The release is horrific. The results are worse.

These reactions are not to be taken lightly. Violent and self-destructive behavior can and does occur. Tardive dyskinesia can and does occur. Permanent damage may result. Many patients experience Tardive withdrawal symptoms for months after careful detoxification. Electric shock sensations, crying, and irritability are common. I have already seen one case of esophageal Tardive dyskinesia from an SSRI.

How can this be avoided? First of all don't take SSRIs unless you really need them. If you do, as loathe as I am to say it, Prozac should be the first choice because of its long half life which allows it to self taper whenever it is stopped. But let's be realistic. If you are one of the millions of the people on these drugs who shouldn't be and the net effect has been that you are numbed out and feel less of everything and care less about anything, which is only slightly better than the distress you were in before treatment, and when you have forgotten your dose for a day or two – ran out or whatever – you have these florid symptoms which your doctor took as proof of your need for the drug or said that you were bipolar, too, and began you on some more nifty keen drugs to treat the "mania" and now your are reading this and are righteously livid and want to get off this junk, what do you do? What you do is continue to take your medicine and seek out a qualified specialist who understands before the fact what you have read in this book thus far and can implement a careful supervised detoxification from these SSRI medications.   Careful tapers with supplemental medications to attack withdrawal symptoms with or without Prozac loading can be used.   Initially I had incorporated a detailed discussion of detoxification regimens but then realized that this would lead some people to try and treat themselves. This is a very bad idea.

CHAPTER TWENTY SEVEN
SUICIDE

Can a medication make you commit suicide? In a narrow sense, no. I know of no such substance that, subsequent to it's administration instantaneously induces a clear cut desire to kill one's self and the related action; suicide. But reality is not so simple.

Some years ago after the introduction of Prozac there was quite a bit of hoopla when allegations were made that several people became suicidal after being treated with this drug, and that some completed suicides occurred. This went back and forth for awhile and then died out after some noted authorities poo pooed the entire notion. These authorities of course either had limited experience with the drug because it had just been released or had experience with the drug because they were paid investigators hired to do pre-market testing of the drug. Remember that at that time the adverse Neuropsychiatric side effects I have described in this book were unknown.

It is well known that the worst complication of depression is suicide. It is also known that suicide can occur during the treatment of depression as a patient's early response to an antidepressant is to be activated or mobilized, to begin to have some energy after having been shut down. This can occur before the patient feels better. Thus they now have the energy to act upon their negativistic and hopeless feelings, unable to comprehend that in fact they are beginning to improve. Another scenario happens when a patient has experienced multiple treatment failures. When a laundry list of treatments have been tried and all have failed for whatever reason, the patient may feel even more hopeless, defective, worthless, and beyond help. They may give up and commit suicide.

Having stated all that is there a drug that specifically puts the thought of suicide in your head? No. Can any drugs promote suicidal behavior? Yes

Previously we stated that a known complication of cluster headaches is suicide. The pain of these headaches is so severe, for so long, that many people have been driven to suicide. Pain and suffering have long been known as precipitants of suicide. Mind you I am not endorsing this route, just describing it. By inference other forms of intense pain and distress may be implicated as potential sources of provocation to suicide attempts.

This may be the case in individuals treated with the wrong antidepressants, specifically the SSRIs when they are not indicated. There are two specific circumstances, both of which have been elucidated previously. One involves the intense acute reaction to initiation of therapy with an SSRI. The second revolves around acute and severe SSRI withdrawal reactions. With the respect to the former I can assert that I have seen patients who have made suicidal gestures and attempts within a day or two of initiation of treatment with an SSRI. Obviously these patients had problems of one sort or another that led to the treatment. Several of them have said that they felt more agitated and out of control after the medication. I infer but cannot prove a causal relationship

I have seen several patients who have made suicidal gestures and attempts upon abrupt cessation of treatment with an SSRI. While they did not know at the time that they were in the throes of an acute and severe SSRI withdrawal syndrome they were able to describe the miserable, horrible feelings that overcame them. Their inability to be still. The escalating fear and dysphoria, the absolute insomnia and their ultimate hopelessness which led up to a self injurious act.

Obviously it is easy to say and no doubt will be said, that this information is anecdotal and that if reflects upon the intrinsic illness and character pathology of the patients and in no way can the patient's action be ascribed to medication. In a very simple minded way that is true. If you are not very simple minded, I encourage you to ponder this carefully.

CHAPTER TWENTY EIGHT
POINTERS

Okay. Here are some pointers that can help you prevent the misery of unnecessary and inappropriate treatment with SSRIs. Above we have already indicated how an adverse reaction to one or two doses of the drugs can warn off the wise. But how not to start?

1] If you suffer from the Neurosomatic problem described in this book, don't take SSRIs.

2] If you've been diagnosed with ADHD, a noradrenalin problem, don't take SSRIs.

3] If you have been addicted to cocaine or amphetamines, or if you tried cocaine and it made you feel good, calmer, focused, better, even very briefly, before it did its bad stuff, don't take SSRIs.

4] If you were begun on an SSRI at a standard dose, seemed to tolerate it, and took it for a month with really no benefit, you probably need different medication. Not another SSRI. The data that purports to demonstrate substantive differences between the SSRIs is very thin and does not establish if any of the responses are truly therapeutic or if the one or another is a more effective goof ball. Remember, the drug companies' own literature establishes that 90% or more of patients with major depression will respond to standard doses of SSRIs (Paxil 20 mg, Prozac 20 mg, Celexa 20 mg, Zoloft 50 mg) within four to eight weeks. High doses of the SSRIs are indicated only in true obsessive compulsive disorder or true anorexia nervosa. If your prescriber continues to increase the dose of an SSRI because it hasn't worked yet, it won't, until you are good and numb. If your doctor doesn't know better and change to a different treatment approach, find a new doctor.

5] If you think you began to have a positive response to an SSRI or were told that you were and after a month or so the

162

"response" attenuates and your symptoms recur and your dose is increased and your symptoms decrease for awhile but your symptoms again emerge so that your dose is increased and your symptoms diminish again for awhile you are in trouble. You are experiencing tachyphylaxis to the dopamine blocking side effects of the SSRI. As your numbness wears off you have the symptom re-emergence often coupled with sub-acute SSRI withdrawal. This is particularly true of the higher potency short acting medications. I have seen innumerable patients on 50 mg to 60 mg per day of Paxil whose primary illness breaks through while simultaneously experiencing SSRI withdrawal symptoms. This is unfortunate to see and difficult to treat. Get help fast.

6] All, repeat, all antidepressants available in the marketplace today take two to four weeks to have a good response and eight weeks for a full response. Therefore it is illogical to increase prescriptions above standard dosage recommendations unless your clinician is remarkably astute. If you have had no response to an antidepressant in a week or so it does not mean that the medicine will not work. You simply have not been on it long enough. If you had an immediate response in say one to three days that wore off after a couple of weeks leading your prescriber to increase the medication every couple of weeks because the response continues to be short lived, you are experiencing tachyphylaxis and the troubles I have described above.

7] Any patient who experiences sudden relief of agitation, depression, anxiety, what have you within a day or two of the initiation of an SSRI is not having a primary therapeutic response. That patient is having an adverse reaction. The acute sudden dopamine blockade induced by the SSRI is numbing the patient, taking away the patient's feelings and acting basically like a goof ball.

IT **IS** ALL IN YOUR HEAD:
A Monograph on Wellness for the New Millennium

LAUNDRY LIST

Over the past decade the SSRIs have been promoted as a cure all for:

1. DEPRESSION
2. ANXIETY
3. PANIC DISORDER
4. SOCIAL ANXIETY
5. PHOBIAS
6. MIGRAINE
7. HEADACHES
8. CHRONIC PAIN
9. PREMENSTRUAL SYNDROME
10. POST TRAUMATIC STRESS DISORDER
11. OBSESSIVE COMPULSIVE DISORDER
12. ANOREXIA NERVOSA
13. BULIMIA
14. BULAREXIA
15. SELF INJURIOUS BEHAVIORS
16. AGGRESSION
17. IMPULSE CONTROL PROBLEMS
18. ADDICTIVE BEHAVIORS
19. GAMBLING
20. MOOD DISORDER DURING PREGNANCY
21. FIBROMYALGIA
22. BORDERLINE PERSONALITY DISORDER
23. DISSOCIATIVE DISORDERS
24. PREMATURE EJACULATION
25. OPPOSITIONAL DEFIANT DISORDER

Quite a list; what? If you do a literature search to discern each and every problem for which the SSRIs have been tried the list would be several yards long. In the minds of many anything is better if sprinkled with Prozac

SSRIs are now being tried **to control undesirable aspects of personality** **and** **behavior** in people without any problem or diagnosis or illness other than that someone else has judged that some facet of their personality and/or behavior is not to their liking and should be treated with a drug to modify or control them to the satisfaction of others. Mind you, this is to control attitudes, behaviors and character, not an illness. Welcome to the monkey house.

The same claim has and can be made about Ritalin in the many cases wherein it has been mis-prescribed to children with a panoply of problems that are not ADHD but does not pertain when the clearly biological disorder of ADHD is present.

SSRIs have been acclaimed as marvelously successful treatment agents in millions of cases where there is no successful treatment whatsoever but in fact a powerful side effect of the drug is at play. SSRIs make many people docile and tame. These drugs numb people. These individuals no longer experience the unpleasant mood or affect or anxiety for which they sought treatment, but in exchange they do not achieve a normal mood range and state. What results is a numbed, neutered la la land where one feels very little about anything. Positive emotions, pleasure, desire, normal urges, normal responses are attenuated severely or in many cases totally obliterated. A blasé indifference is induced which creates hordes of people who once were troubled and though they may be troubled still care not one whit about it and for the most part don't care enough about almost anything to do something about it. They lumber through life like so many lobotomized capons, untroubled and untroubleable. This is truly Novocain for the brain.

CHAPTER TWENTY NINE
THE BIG PICTURE

It's time to step back and take a look at the big picture. There is a disease entity which I have chosen to call Neurosomatic. It is a singular entity with polymorphous symptomatology, most of which has heretofore been seen as separate and unrelated illnesses and treated as such, as separate and unrelated illnesses. Most of them have been ascribed to a functional, psychosomatic, or psychophysiologic source, always impugning the character of the patient.

We have looked at the case histories of sample patients which illustrate how this disease can present in many ways. We have seen how grossly it has been misunderstood and mismanaged.

This is a brain/body disease. It is not a mind/body disease. Somewhere in the brain's universe something is a bit out of whack. There is an imbalance or deficiency in the noradrenalin transmitter pathways. There are related imbalances in systems that inhibit or calm other parts of the brain. There is a dramatic dysregulation of the autonomic nervous system. The hypothalamus with its abundant thermostats does not sense or respond precisely and abnormalities in the hypothalamic pituitary adrenal axis are seen. Thyroid aberrations are seen in mood disorders as well as abnormal cortisone cycling and abnormalities in glucose metabolism. There are abnormalities in other circadian rhythms as well such as those involving sleep.

Neurosomatic individuals are highly allergic individuals. Clearly it is not a coincidence that histamine which is released excessively and in abundance in patients with allergies is also a primary element of many Neurosomatic symptoms including the migraine cascade and various gastrointestinal symptoms and asthma.

IT **IS** ALL IN YOUR HEAD:
A Monograph on Wellness for the New Millennium

The primary Neurosomatic symptoms include depression, anxiety, panic, headaches and migraine, sugar binges, poor quality, restless sleep, attention deficit hyperactivity disorder and gastrointestinal problems. Secondary symptoms include aches and pains, TMJ syndrome, high blood pressure, and allergies.

The successful treatment of this disorder hinges on central noradrenalin mobilization. Not more serotonin. With a short list of available options one does not have to grope around for choices. The sleep and anxiety component of the Neurosomatic Syndrome require increased GABA activity. Not more serotonin. The attentional symptoms often need a direct stimulant. Not more serotonin.

Yes I assert that a great number of people to this point in time have been misunderstood, misdiagnosed, mismanaged and maligned while suffering from this disease. I further assert that a great number of people will do very well and be normal and happy and regular folks on a steady dose of a stimulant and/or a sedative. By gosh, some folks will do fine on long term Valium and/or long term Adderall.

Unquestionably the puritans and sadists and sanctimonious folks who don't like this idea will disagree. And the nasty types who intimidate physicians and threaten their licenses when they give terminal patients enough pain medicine may attack physicians who treat this disease properly. Hopefully not. Those who are fixated on unbleached flour and blue green algae should give this a careful think before they reject it. It might make their child's life easier.

No this book is not a controlled study. It is quite scientific though in an old fashioned way and reflects more than twenty years of patient examination and treatment. I encourage my colleagues to stop and reflect on their own experience and view their patients within this framework. Try it on and try it out. You will be surprised and pleased. Ignore if you will the proponents of the SSRIs as the great panacea of the new millennium. Ignore the drug reps and the advertisements and the paid investigators who beat the drums for them. Think and enquire and talk with patients and learn the difference between a genuine response to an SSRI as opposed to the numbed out, feel less of everything, really don't care much about anything anymore goof ball effect.

Personally I am distressed every time I see a teenager who was assessed for depression or anxiety or anger or acting out and was begun on Paxil and literally escalated wildly out of control and then got diagnosed as bipolar and zapped with major tranquilizers and was begun on Depakote or Lithium or whatever. Or the incredible agony of the next child who comes to me on 50 mg of Paxil or 200 mg of Zoloft and has to be detoxified painfully and tediously over two months or more and whose proper treatment really can't commence until the detoxification is well along. Or the next person in florid SSRI withdrawal brought to the emergency room by the police. Maybe you want to make sure your physician has read this book before you see him or her again. Make sure that you are heard.

CHAPTER THIRTY
HISTORICAL NOTES AND ANECDOTES: FEELING GOOD?
NAUGHTY NAUGHTY!

Diet pills are bad. Immoral, improper, illegal. People should just grit their teeth and not eat so much or get used to it and just be fat and sassy. Doctors who prescribe diet pills are unethical sleazy characters who work out of grimy little offices where they see forty patients an hour and literally sell prescriptions.

Cocaine and amphetamine mobilize (cause to be released) noradrenalin and dopamine from neurons in the brain. Not serotonin. Ritalin mobilizes noradrenaline, some dopamine, and a tad of serotonin. You may be surprised to know that not everyone gets a kick out of these drugs. This is <u>not</u> a promotional message for these substances but it is a declaratory statement. For some these substances induce a sense of calm and ease. Others become irritable and dysphoric. Yet others become somnolent. There is not a single uniform response to these drugs. **NO.** This does not mean it is okay for some folks to use these substances ad lib. It does mean that not everyone has the same neurochemistry or brain chemistry. Different strokes for different folks. Yes indeed some people can get high, abuse and become addicted to these drugs. But for another segment of the population, they can't figure out what the others see in them. In a word; feh!

Attempts to manufacture diet pills that have no risk of addiction or abuse by anyone have involved the addition of other chemicals to a basic amphetamine core. Generally this involves the use of a potent serotonin mobilizing elements which seem to blunt or block the potentially pleasurable and abusable aspects of the amphetamine. Redux and Phen Phen are examples. Both were withdrawn because of highly toxic side effects.

169

A similar attitude has been put forth with respect to sedatives. It's not okay to use them on a regular basis even if they make you, well, okay and normal. It is acceptable to try cumbersome antidepressants if you suffer chronic anxiety problems whether they work or not. Yet as one wag put it, "it seems that a lot of people's brains were born about 5 mg of Valium short".

There has been a social and legal discouragement of the use of anorectics (appetite suppressants) and anxiolytics (anxiety suppressants). The chronic use of a pill to suppress appetite or to suppress anxiety is seen as bad, immoral, and illegal. Physicians who prescribe such medications run the risk of severe punishment.

What's in a name? Anorectic means appetite suppressant. Anxiolytic means to eradicate anxiety. What if these medications were considered modulators. Not suppressants but modulators. What if there were a group of medications that normalized or modulated appetite. And another group that normalized or modulated anxiety within a normal range. Such a concept would be totally in concert with the body's need for homeostasis and balance.

An abundance of medications are used to modulate and stabilize within a normal range many of the body's systems that have become ill. Medicines to modulate blood pressure, blood sugar, heart rate and rhythm, and the metabolism of various substances such as uric acid which can cause gout. One would not want one's blood pressure eradicated. Nor would one want one's blood sugar lysed. Either would be fatal.

But such things as blood pressure and blood sugar and heart rhythm are manifestations of **real** medical illnesses. Illnesses that affect and afflict your body. Anxiety and appetite and attention and the multiplicity of symptoms that comprise the Neurosomatic Syndrome have always been said to be "in your head". They have been scurrilously said to be functional, psychosomatic psychophysiologic or hypochondriacal. Psychopharmacotherapeutic treatment to modulate within a normal range, or to establish homeostasis in the brain and body are seen as improper, immoral, unethical and illegal. It is just this stance that facilitates the misidentification and misunderstanding of Neurosomatics and fosters a great deal of the maltreatment so widely seen today.

CHAPTER THIRTY ONE
NOVOCAIN FOR THE BRAIN

Attempts to treat the symptoms of the Neurosomatic Syndrome are as old as history and probably older. Reference has been made previously to the use of alcohol and various plants that had calming and sedative effects. Others are available which have stimulating effects including ephedrine and cocaine. The regular school of medicine in the twentieth century has focused on purified pharmacotherapeutic interventions. This has been hampered however by social mores.

Before and after World War II there was extensive use of barbiturates for the treatment of anxiety. Small amounts of opiates and cocaine were used in the treatment of depression. The physicians of the time had no concept of biogenic amines. Nor did they know about endorphins. They did know what seemed to work.

After World War II the use of medium acting barbiturates such as Butisol diminished as a new group of medications emerged, the carbamates. These included Miltown and Equanil. These medications were wildly prescribed and to some degree abused. In the 1960's a new group of medications was developed, the benzodiazepines. Librium and Valium overtook the carbamates because they were seen as less toxic, safer medications with greater therapeutic indices. However some people did abuse these medications, get high and there was a great push not to use these medications on a long term basis even in patients who might benefit from controlled, modest, long term prescriptions.

There evolved an unfortunate prescription pattern wherein many physicians would not use minor tranquilizers for more than a few weeks. But what of the patients whose symptoms of anxiety and depression and insomnia and other Neurosomatic complaints didn't go away in three weeks. The answer was to use major tran-quilizers. The major tranquilizers or anti-psychotic neuroleptic drugs were substituted. These drugs are never addictive and cannot be abused. And they will whack just about anybody. The immediate effect of these drugs, at the time Thorazine, Stelazine, and Mellaril to be followed by Haldol, Navane and others, is to induce immediate dopamine blockade and make a person blotto. It is this effect, the taking away of all feelings, that leads many intelligent but troubled schizophrenics to refuse anti-psychotic medications because they do not like it when they have no feelings. They would rather be ill and have their emotions than have nothing.

Most of the prescribers of these medications gave them to non-schizophrenic patients. The results were that most people didn't take them for very long because of the unpleasant side effects which we have detailed previously and many patients were injured through the development of Tardive dyskinesia, Tardive akathisia and other long term neurologic side effects.

Attempts were made to use the older tricyclic antidepressants to treat some chronic anxiety states and some small success was achieved in small groups of patients. But even then little attention was paid by most clinicians to the differences between noradrenergic and serotonergic medications and the appropriate prescriptions of them.

With the advent of the SSRIs a fascinating phenomenon occurred. These supposedly very safe medications seemed to take care of so much. Patients with a huge laundry list of presenting complaints could be started on one or another of the new SSRI medications and within a few days be controlled. This was seen as a majestic therapeutic triumph. People's unpleasant feelings suddenly went away. They went away not to be replaced by normal feelings. They went away to be replaced by no feelings. Remember that this phenomenon occurs to many people within one, two or three doses of an SSRI. By definition it is not a therapeutic response. It is an adverse response from dopamine blockade yet it is misinterpreted by hundreds of thousands of prescribers as a dramatic therapeutic coup. Patients suffering from a panoply of symptoms and complaints, many of them related in terms of the Neurosomatic Syndrome and many of them unrelated are all numbed on an SSRI. Ask yourself or people you know who are or have been on SSRIs what it was like and a remarkable preponderance will say that they had no feelings. Nothing much bothered them. They just didn't care. Everything was sort of okay. They just went through life. It may be that there are some people with primitive character disorders who are unable to deal with any difficult emotions whatsoever and might appreciate having their emotions excised as if they were a tumor. But most human beings do not agree with this concept.

Millions of people throughout the world are taking a daily dose of an SSRI goof ball to suppress whatever troubled them at some point. Some of them have a true therapeutic response. But a staggering number have a chronic side effect which renders them asexual, insomniac, overweight, detached and bland. There was something prescient in Vonnegut's work.

CHAPTER THIRTY TWO
THE PIECE MEAL APPROACH

The present symptom organ approach is basically a piece meal approach. A symptom or complaint is addressed by a generalist or specialist in a very narrow focus. In some cases a good result may occur. This is most apparent when a patient does not have the Neurosomatic Syndrome and in fact is an individual who has a single complaint.

Patients with migraine headaches and no other complaints may do very well with traditional migraine treatment. Someone with a panic disorder and obsessive compulsive disorder may do quite well with traditional treatments and SSRIs.

But several symptoms of the Neurosomatic Syndrome do not occur autonomously. What this means is that any patient who has certain cardinal features of the Neurosomatic Syndrome has the Neurosomatic Syndrome. What might these be?

We have spent a good deal of time developing a diagnostic scheme and a Neurosomatic points scale. This is a useful, educational and diagnostic tool. What it means is that any patient who presents with a complaint or symptom or diagnosis on the list of Neurosomatic complaints should be examined thoroughly for the possible presence of the Neurosomatic Syndrome. This is necessary to separate out patients with a pure form of migraine or panic disorder or colitis from those with the Neurosomatic Syndrome. This will help clarify and improve assessment and treatment.

There are however symptoms and diagnoses which by their very presence suggest the Neurosomatic Syndrome. These include attention deficit hyperactivity disorder; fibromyalgia; headaches; and bulimia.

The very strongest diagnostic indicator is ADHD. The sec

ond strongest is fibromyalgia. The mixed headaches and bulimia are a bit weaker.

There is no question that ADHD is a biological medical diagnosis. It is not always correctly identified and treated. The failure to understand it and the fact that it is a Neurosomatic diagnosis renders the treatment of the presenting complaint suboptimal in many, many cases leading to questions about the accuracy of the diagnosis.

By the present diagnostic criteria not every patient who has the Neurosomatic Syndrome will qualify formally for the diagnosis of ADHD. However careful examination of any patient with the Neurosomatic Syndrome will reveal a significant number of attentional symptoms. Looking at it from the other side every patient who meets the diagnosis for ADHD will have sufficient Neurosomatic symptoms to qualify for that diagnosis.

Obviously age is a factor here. In the assessment of small children they may not yet have experienced many of the Neurosomatic complaints or they may not have been understood as such.

My assessment of patients with ADHD of all races, ages and genders reveals that greater than 90% of them have non-restorative sleep/periodic limb movement disorder. They may or may not have active flopping around but most of those who don't have limb movement will have bruxism. A small portion will have neither limb movements or bruxism but they will still have poor quality or "light" sleep with difficulties falling asleep, difficulty staying asleep, diminished or no dream time and they are grumpy and tired in the morning. As they get older their exhaustion increases.

Many patients and parents have to be convinced of this in an empirical manner. They are loathe to admit that there is a sleep problem present until a trial of something like Neurontin demonstrates a dramatic and positive change in the patient's sleep. As discussed before cases of enuresis and encopresis as well as various parasomnias such as sleep walking and sleep talking in children and adolescents are immediately corrected.

Careful examination of ADHD patients reveals a very high incidence of headaches which usually are called migraines but which in fact often are mixed headaches with mid-line, central, bitemporal or behind the eyes headaches which are the classic sleep disorder headache in some cases commingled with unilateral and extremely unpleasant migraine headaches.

ADHD patients are notoriously anxious and moody. Often they are misdiagnosed and/or over diagnosed with the "co-morbid" diagnosis of bipolar disorder. Significant gastrointestinal problems are present. Adolescent and adult patients frequently have been evaluated and treated for irritable bowel syndrome, ulcer complaints, and reflux esophagitis. Many of the children diagnosed with ADHD have "nervous stomachs". They get tummy aches easily, vomit easily, spend a lot of time going to the school nurse and/or miss school frequently. Whether diagnosed with "fibromyalgia" or not, many of the adult patients are very poor sleepers, frequently hypnotic dependent, who are tired and achy in the morning. Many are diagnosed as having some form of arthritis.

The symptom/organ approach to ADHD taken by most practitioners is to treat the attention problem with something like a stimulant or maybe antidepressants. The other symptoms are seen as irrelevant or possibly as co-morbid and usually treated by other practitioners leading to the hodgepodge we have discussed above. The focused Neurosomatic approach which addresses the central brain/body problem corrects the full range and scope of the disorder with much less medication, fewer side effects and fewer consultants.

More than 90% of the patients seen in my office with

177

supposed fibromyalgia have the Neurosomatic Syndrome and have had dramatic results when treated as such. The less than 10% who have not improved seem to fall into one or two categories. On the one hand are patients who demonstrate an excellent objective response to treatment with diminution and resolution of virtually all complaints but who are never satisfied with the treatment. It is never good enough. Whatever progress is made and however much simpler the regimen becomes and how ever better the patient feels and functions they don't like it. This suggests significant character pathology usually in the spectrum of a borderline personality disorder.

The other group of patients do not have this character dysfunction and do not get better. These patients have some other form of "fibromyalgia". My suspicion at this time is that these patients have a true inflammatory process related to an occult infection. This is most likely attributable to something like Lyme Disease or other obscure infectious processes as yet poorly understood and not effectively treated.

As always with the symptom/organ approach the present traditional approach to the fibromyalgia patient involves a consultant prescribing for the symptoms of fibromyalgia usually with further destruction of sleep architecture, increasing distress, excessive medication dependence often with narcotics involved, and progressive disability. The related Neurosomatic symptoms, particularly the headache, gastrointestinal complaints, anxiety, and depression often are made worse by the serotonergic agents prescribed and the care is confused by the multiple consultants and prescribers addressing each of these symptoms as a co-morbid diagnosis.

Mixed headaches are problematic. The patient who presents with a complaint of headaches warrants a very careful history and examination. It is of great importance to delineate the frequency, intensity, quality, pattern, location, and timing of headaches. We have pointed out that many Neurosomatic patients have migraine and/or cluster headaches in conjunction with dense, boring, painful mid-line headaches which are usually called migraines although sometimes when they present a bit farther back are mistaken for muscle tension headache. Very often neither the migraine nor the mid-line headache respond very well or very long to multiple typical migraine regimens. Pure migraine might but the mid-line headache will not respond unless the sleep disorder is identified and treated. Failure to do this leads to progressively complicated treatment and progressively confounded patients.

Remember that the SSRIs and other serotonergic drugs so commonly prescribed in these circumstances induce alpha delta sleep, disrupting deep sleep and diminishing REM sleep and also causing actual REM suppression.

Thus if a patient's headache history is consistent with multiple types of headaches, in particular the sleep disorder headache, further questioning with respect to Neurosomatic complaints is warranted.

Bulimia has been a difficult problem for a long time. It really has nothing to do with true anorexia nervosa. As described above the pattern typically emerges over a period of time related to carbohydrate cravings and overeating which leads to bingeing, complicated by autonomic nervous system reactivity and cessation of parasympathetic function with an intense need to purge the stomach. For 25 years studies in the treatment of bulimia have shown little benefit from most standard therapies. Of course there are studies that suggest that SSRIs over a short period of time have shown some benefit. This is entirely consistent with the side effect of dopamine blockade inducing some initial symptom suppression followed by the recurrence of symptoms as tachyphylaxis occurs. SSRIs have not shown any long term benefit here.

While all noradrenergic agents are formally contraindicated in bulimia and eating disorders (contraindicated means you shouldn't use them) I and others have found great success using Wellbutrin and some stimulants to mobilize noradrenalin, suppress anxiety and carbohydrate cravings, diminish autonomic lability, and in conjunction with correct treatment of the Neurosomatic Syndrome resolve the problem. This is done with proper informed consent. I have had no adverse reactions.

In summary the presence of any Neurosomatic symptoms warrants a reasonable enquiry into the possible existence of a Neurosomatic Syndrome in every patient. The presence of the cardinal symptoms of ADHD, fibromyalgia, mixed headaches and bulimia suggests the presence of the Neurosomatic Syndrome until proven otherwise.

CHAPTER THIRTY THREE
HISTORICAL NOTES AND PATIENT QUOTES

Many women with the Neurosomatic Syndrome have a history of both misdiagnosed eating disorders (they really do have the sugar binge thing) and post partum depression (that did not respond well to SSRIs). They report that when they are pregnant they are not moody or depressed and that they have no urge to binge. Clearly the hormonal and metabolic changes of pregnancy ameliorate the problem.

Woman with Stein Leventhal Syndrome appear to have a poorly defined abnormality of glucose metabolism. I have seen several dozen of them with the Neurosomatic Syndrome. I have not yet seen a patient with Stein Leventhal Syndrome who does not have the Neurosomatic Syndrome. Patients with the Neurosomatic Syndrome do have a disorder or carbohydrate metabolism. Warrants some thought. I'm thinking about it.

Patients often can be funny in what they disclose. You can ask them straight away if they have migraine or irritable bowels or restless legs and so forth and so on and they say absolutely not. Then some weeks later they sort of remember.

Mort, aged 67 when diagnosed. Began Neurontin, " . . . best damn night's sleep since Truman was president."

Jane, aged 37, removed from Paxil, etc. for treatment of bulimia and depression. On Wellbutrin and Neurontin. Stable, no binges, steadily loses weight towards normal range, sleep dramatically better, . . . "and you know what my irritable bowels have settled down for the first time since first grade."

Chaya, aged 11, on Neurontin, "wow I had my first dream since I was five!"

Pierre, aged 32, on Neurontin and Ritalin, " . . boy is my wife happy I don't thrash around anymore. She was afraid I'd break her nose again." Again? !

And hundreds of remarks, a mixture of anger, resentment, melancholy and wistfulness about how life might have been different if the diagnosis had been made and proper treatment rendered when "I" was a kid, in school, before, earlier, you know, maybe college, gee whiz . . .

CHAPTER THIRTY FOUR
REFLECTIONS THROUGH THE LOOKING GLASS

As we have discussed Neurosomatics and put together the pieces of its puzzle it has become increasingly clear that the information and inferences have for the most part been apparent for a long time. What has established the Neurosomatic Syndrome is a different perspective on the data. Mention has been made of the manner in which sleep studies have been interpreted in patients with "fibromyalgia" and the Neurosomatic Syndrome. Alpha delta sleep and prolonged REM latencies with diminished dream sleep have been interpreted as a sign of a tense and anxious patient. Understanding Neurosomatics, the idea that this is a brain/body, not a mind/body problem gives the opposite interpretation. That is of course that the abnormal sleep rhythms seen are primary manifestations of an imbalance in the central nervous system which is experienced and expressed by the patient's mind as anxiety.

Other behaviors and inferences can be re-evaluated through this looking glass and seen to be entirely consistent with this point of view. A preponderance of individuals with ADHD, anxiety, depression and to some degree migraine feel better when they exercise. The act of exercising mobilizes the production and release of adrenergic agents within the body as well as endorphins and induces a sense of well being as well as a remarkable calm. The vigorous stimulation which excites some people actually has a calming effect on the Neurosomatic patient. This is because the innate chemical imbalance has been temporarily corrected by the intense release of these chemical transmitters and homeostasis and a good calm normal feeling is achieved albeit transiently

Drug abuse in Neurosomatic patients revolves around two major chemical groups. On the one hand stimulants of any sort that increase the release of noradrenalin and to a lesser degree dopamine make the patient feel better, not necessarily high mind you but better. Because of the rapid attenuation of the positive effects in conjunction with the addictive potential of these illicit substances the process escalates complicated by rebound depression and tachyphylaxis.

The other hand reflects excessive use of alcohol and sedatives for the purpose of diminishing or containing anxiety. There is abundant clinical and social data to support this.

Neurosomatic patients feel better when they are active, moving, or doing something even if that something is intense cerebral activity. The psychologists would suggest that this is because they are distracted from their problems. I would submit that this is because the brain activity increases the release of the needed chemicals and establishes a more normal homeostatic balance during the period of activity.

These and many other simple observations can be made. It is interesting to reject the psychological interpretation and reverse direction to a biological frame of reference.

CHAPTER THIRTY FIVE
YOU STILL CAN'T EAT AND RUN

Great. You learned that you have this Neurosomatic Syndrome. You found a qualified specialist to help you safely unload that Paxil and Depakote and Fioricet and Immitrex and Elavil and Trazadone and, well, you can fill it in. And you are doing so much better on a very simple regimen. Oh, say, some useful combination of noradrenergic and a GABAergic. Terrific. You still can't eat and run.

This brain-body problem is stable. What a relief! What a pleasure to sleep and to wake refreshed and to be in better control and for those headaches and cramps and pains to be a fading memory and the pharmacy bill to have shrunken lower than your mortgage. Amazing.

This doesn't mean it's wise or healthy to fight traffic at noon between appointments as you try to dictate into your micro cassette and talk on your cell phone and eat a pastrami sandwich. If you do, please expect your body to tell you it's a very bad idea, your new diagnosis and new treatment notwithstanding. Then, when you complain, and your physician recommends you to see a good psychiatrist – do.

IT **IS** ALL IN YOUR HEAD:
A Monograph on Wellness for the New Millennium

APPENDIX

THEORETICAL GUIDELINES FOR THE TREATMENT OF SSRI WITHDRAWAL

In the pages to follow will be described a coherent strategy for the safe and effective treatment of SSRI withdrawal. This has been developed in the treatment of hundreds of patients whose misfortune it has been to have been placed upon improper--and usually excessive--regimens of these nasty drugs. We will review the drugs, the pathophysiology, the neurochemistry and the treatment options. The discussion will be blunt. There will not be the use of *italics* to discuss the more technical aspects; this data must be apprehended in total.

!WARNING!
THESE ARE GUIDELINES. UNDER NO CIRCUMSTANCE SHOULD THE FOLLOWING INFORMATION AND DISCUSSION BE TAKEN AS A TREATMENT PLAN OR A TREATMENT RECOMMENDATION. IF YOU REQUIRE TREATMENT FOR THE DISCONTINUATION OF ANY MEDICATION, INCLUDING THE SSRIs, YOU MUST, REPEAT, MUST SEEK OUT THE EXPERTISE OF AN AUTHORITY IN PSYCHOPHARMACOLOGY OR A RELATED FIELD WITH EXTENSIVE EXPERIENCE IN SSRI DETOXIFICATION. IT IS INADVISABLE TO SEEK TREATMENT WITH THE PRESCRIBER WHO CAUSED THE PROBLEM IN THE FIRST PLACE. DO NOT EVER ATTEMPT TO SELF-TREAT. WHAT FOLLOWS IS NOT A TREATMENT RECOMMENDATION

OR A TREATMENT PLAN FOR ANYONE.

The SSRIs available today in the United States are: Prozac; Zoloft; Paxil: Celexa; Luvox and Effexor. As of this writing a congener of Celexa is about to be released. The serotonergic drug Serzone also has some SSRI like effects and should be considered in this discussion.

All of the SSRIs are purported to block re-uptake of serotonin by the afferent neuron (the nerve cell which sends the message to the receiving, or efferent Neuron), while eventually increasing the sensitivity of serotonin receptors to available serotonin on the efferent neuron. All of which has something to do with the induction of serotonin syndrome in some patients but absolutely nothing to do with SSRI addiction and withdrawal.

SSRI addiction and withdrawal are manifestations of the phenomenon of dopamine blockade, breakthrough (tachyphylaxis) and rebound. For the most part these effects are identical to the awful side effects experienced by schizophrenic patients treated with anti-psychotic, neuroleptic medication (neuroleptic, by the by means to cause neurologic [brain!] damage). Except that this misery occurs rapidly in individuals highly susceptible to the toxic side effects of neuroleptics. It has been well known for decades that non-schizophrenic patients, patients with affective/mood disorders and patients subjected to pulse exposures of neuroleptics are far more sensitive to neurotoxicity and Tardive processes that are schizophrenic patients committed to long term, steady treatment.

Hence most patients for whom SSRIs are prescribed are the most likely to be at risk for neurotoxic effects of dopamine blockade. To make matters worse, most patients are given absurdly high doses of SSRIs as the unwitting prescribers chase the primary symptoms of disease not really amenable to the SSRI while simultaneously treating the tachyphylactic dopamine symptom breakthrough.

Another miserable phenomenon occurs with high dose SSRI mal-treatment. This is chronic sub-acute withdrawal. Patients who have been maxed out on stupendous SSRI doses (i.e. 60-80 mg of Paxil or Celexa, 200 mg of Zoloft, 300-400 mg of Luvox, 300 mg or more of Effexor, and so forth) experience: 1} symptoms of their primary illness; 2} agitation, insomnia, sweating, and a myriad of other complaints from a combination of dopamine blockade and excessive serotonin (serotonin syndrome); and 3} sub-acute SSRI withdrawal as tachyphylaxis occurs and dopamine blockade breaks through with symptoms of akathisia, dysphoria, restlessness, insomnia, GI distress, agitation, crying, etc. All of which are misinterpreted as the patient's primary illness--depression, anxiety, panic, bipolar, character disorder, eating disorder, what have you-- and justify more polypharmacy to treat these symptoms.

The material differences between the SSRIs pertain to potency and half-life. Potency means how strong per dose. Thus 20 mg of Prozac is roughly equivalent to 50 mg of Zoloft in terms of efficacy. The term used to describe this is milligram potency. Paxil and Effexor are the most potent per milligram. Effexor is harder to appreciate because it is a combination drug, but the SSRI component is horrible.

Half-life describes the time required for one half of the total amount of a drug in a persons body to be metabolized and excreted. In simple terms, if one takes a single 20 mg dose of Paxil, in five days your body will have disposed of 10 mg. In five days more another 2.5 mg is cleared. And so forth.

Awareness of these two concepts, milligram potency and half-life, foster understanding of the problems of SSRI withdrawal. Simply put, when a very potent drug blocks the dopamine pathway, and then goes away abruptly, it is as if a dam has broken and and a powerful destructive flood cascades out.

Be aware. Withdrawal from heroin, treated or not, takes 72 to 96 hours and you are over the hill. Alcohol withdrawal--which is very, very dangerous if done cold-turkey and requires medical supervision--peaks at 48 hours and is usually completed in 96 hours. SSRI withdrawal generally takes at least four **weeks** and residual, **Tardive** symptoms may continue and dwindle, or not, for several months.

Essentially there are three ways to come off of an SSRI. They are:

1} Abrupt, cold-turkey discontinuation. This is not advisable. In most circumstances terrible abstinence symptoms occur.

2} A gradual taper of the SSRI supplemented with several other substances to diminish neurotoxicity and attenuate the abstinence symptoms.

3} Just as number 2 above, but with the addition of Prozac loading.

A discussion will ensue of the various SSRIs and the different strategies for withdrawal. Again, these are not treatment recommendations for anyone.

We will deal first with Prozac. Prozac actually is a cumbersome drug insofar as it has metabolites with half-lives of about five weeks. The good news is that an individual treated with a proper therapeutic dose of Prozac--20 mg per day--usually can discontinue that dose and it will self-taper, dwindle away over a month or so without appreciable abstinence symptoms. The bad news is that any side effects one has experienced from the Prozac will continue and dwindle away over the same period of time. And there remains a risk of Tardive processes down the road, even though the dopamine blockade is released very slowly. Furthermore any new treatment, say for the Neurosomatic Syndrome, will be delayed and confounded by the intrusive and disruptive effects of the SSRI as it goes away, and as the brain seeks to re-establish a baseline equilibrium after it is gone. Many patient's will require supplemental therapy to treat withdrawal. This will be described below.

Unhappily patients treated with supra-therapeutic Prozac doses, 30-100 mg per day cannot stop treatment and expect it to self-taper. The symptoms of SSRI withdrawal generally emerge. Such patients should have their Prozac dose reduced by no more than 20 mg each week, receiving as necessary supplemental therapies.

All of the remaining SSRIs require detoxification. Unquestionably Paxil is the most miserable drug, followed closely by Effexor, Celexa, Zoloft and Luvox. Paxil appears to be more potent than any of the others and to go away with celerity.

The first half-life of this group of drugs is about five days. Hence never, repeat, never make a dose reduction in less than five days. Go slower if needed, never go faster. Beware; the incidence of abstinence symptoms and Tardive processes increases at the back end of the detoxification process. I postulate this to be a function of the greater percentage decreases in total drug burden as the doses are stepped down. And some of the most miserable Tardive effects occur in the month after the drug has been discontinued and neurochemical equilibrium (hopefully) occurs. Most notable are sudden crying, mood lability, poor memory and no concentration, and precipitate suicidal impulses.

Dosage reduction must be methodical and slow. Patients must be reminded and warned not to push it lest they end up in florid withdrawal and indescribable distress.

Examples of tapering schedules at five day steps might be: from Paxil 80 mg per day; 60 mg to 40 mg to 30 mg to 20 mg to 10 mg to 5 mg and then stop. A similar schedule can apply to Celexa. For Zoloft and Luvox, again at five day steps, a taper might be: 150 mg to 100 mg to 75 mg to 50 mg to 25 mg and so forth. Fractional doses and slower tapers may be needed. Effexor should be given in the regular, not the long acting form, in twice daily doses. Starting at 300 mg the total daily dose might be decreased as: 250 mg to 200 mg to 150 mg to 100 mg to 50 mg to 25 mg and stop.

Supplemental therapies include anti-oxidant vitamins such as Vitamin E 400 iu twice daily and Vitamin C 500 mg twice daily. These may help diminish neurotoxicty.

The best agents to treat acute withdrawal symptoms on as add needed basis (p.r.n. in the parlance) are the long acting benzodiazepines Valium and Klonopin. These drugs provide a combination of increased GABA activity, (GABA again being the brain's primary <u>inhibitory</u> neurotransmitter) and some sedation. They are preferable to any of the shorter acting benzodiazepines because of their long half lives and slow excretion. They work longer and are much less likely to have a bounce effect. With proper supervision there is no risk of addiction. Xanax should never be used. It is a triazolobenzodiazepine and far too addictive to add to the mix. Never use anti-psychotic, neuroleptic medication. Obviously the dopamine blockade induced by such drugs would buy some relief at the cost of lengthening the detoxification process and potentially worsening the risk of Tardive processes.

Typically I have found doses of Klonopin 0.5 mg to 1 mg, or Valium 2.5 mg to 5 mg every six hours as needed to be helpful. When they are not, stronger remedies are needed. There are two options I have found useful.

IT **IS** ALL IN YOUR HEAD:
A Monograph on Wellness for the New Millennium

The anticholinergic drug Cogentin can provide relief from the akathisia and subjective dysphoria that so devastates many people. A dose of 0.5 mg to 1 mg every 12 hours as needed appears to work. There are many possible side-effects and potential problems with this drug for many patients. It must be supervised closely by an expert very familiar with them.

When the above remedies fail a patient must be seen in an Emergency Room and maybe hospitalized. Parenteral (injected) Sodium Amytal in doses up to 250 mg every six to eight hours will provide swift and safe relief, in the properly monitored and supervised environment.

Prozac loading: pros and cons. The concept of Prozac loading is to replace the tapering short half life drug with the ultra long-acting SSRI Prozac. Then the Prozac self tapers (see above). Typically I prescribe 40 mg per day for the first two weeks of the detoxification. This is sufficient for most patients.

Pros: Appears to diminish overall distress in some patients as it attenuates the release of the dopamine blockade. It is highly recommended in children, adolescents and adults with certain character pathology; infantile, borderline, inadequate and histrionic.

Cons: Can place significant stress on liver function in some individuals with liver disease and or who are on several medications. It may exacerbate some SSRI side-effects for a protracted time; for example causing alpha intrusion and disturbing sleep. And it will delay for another month the time when definitive, pro-active treatment can really penetrate and work.

Depending upon the condition of the patient and the clinical situation new treatment may begin as detoxification proceeds. Wellbutrin may be initiated and load as an SSRI is weaned away to have a therapeutic response begin as soon as possible. Neurontin and Gabitril, used to correct PLMD generally will not work during the worst parts of SSRI withdrawal. The benzodiazepines provide better relief through their sedative effects. Nothing works very well for sleep at this time and care must be taken to avoid the development of hypnotic dependence.

It must be kept in mind that Tardive processes, both subtle and profound may continue for months. It is critical that the patient be treated by a skilled Psychiatrist or Neurospsychiatrist with abundant clinical experience in these matters to avoid the pitfalls of misperceiving these symptoms as primary Neuropsychiatric illness and the clinical acumen to treat these difficult iatrogenic problems as safely and simply as possible.

Please re-read the warning above. These are general guidelines. Never, never, never, ever alter your treatment independently. Do so only under the careful supervision of a capable physician.

IT **IS** ALL IN YOUR HEAD:
A Monograph on Wellness for the New Millennium

IT **IS** ALL IN YOUR HEAD:
A Monograph on Wellness for the New Millennium

IT **IS** ALL IN YOUR HEAD:
A Monograph on Wellness for the New Millennium

BIBLIOGRAPHY

The Wisdom of the Body, Cannon, Walter, M. D. (original publication 1932), W. W. Norton & Co., New York, 1963

Psychosomatic Medicine, Alexander, Franz, M. D., W. W. Norton & Co., New York, 1950

Three Essays on Sexuality, Freud, Sigmund, M. D., (original publication 1905), The Hogarth Press, London, 1953

DSM-II, Second Edition,American Psychiatric Association, Washington, D. C. 1968

DSM-III, American Psychiatric Association, Washington, D. C.,1980

DSM-III-R, American Psychiatric Association, Washington, D. C.,1987

DSM-IV, American Psychiatric Association, Washington, D. C.,1994

DSM-IV-TR, American Psychiatric Association, Washington, D. C., 2000

Welcome to the Monkey House, Vonnegut, Kurt, Jr., Dell Publishing Co., New York, 1970

IT **IS** ALL IN YOUR HEAD:
A Monograph on Wellness for the New Millennium

IT **IS** ALL IN YOUR HEAD:
A Monograph on Wellness for the New Millennium

AKNOWLEDGEMENTS

The author would like to thank Dr. Daryl Erickson for his support, criticism and encouragement. Connie McKay provided invaluable assistance in the preparation of the manuscript and it's several iterations.

Carola, my wife furnished incisive editorial insight and superhuman tolerance and support. Without the technical and artistic wizardry of my children, Gabriella, Marissa and Jory--who actually know how to work computers and other newfangled gizmos (peripherals?)--this project would still be in Number 2 pencil. And I thank my patients from whom I have learned so much.

Jory F. Goodman, M. D. March, 2002